Nature's Garden of Crystals

Nature's Garden

of

Crystals

Edited by Vandall T. King

Newryqs Press
Rochester, New York

2011

About the front cover: Galena and Fluorite, Sub-Rosiclare Level, Poe Pod, Annabel Lee Mine. Ozark-Mahoning Company, Harris Creek District, Southern Illinois, USA. Fluorite is 30.5 cm wide and 33 cm tall. Largest Galena is 9.5 cm x 10.2 cm. Mined 1988. The unique beauty of this specimen immediately captured us when Gary Fleck, owner of Inner Earth, generously presented the mineral; it was not for sale at that time but we were eager to see every beautiful mineral he owned. Down the road Gary decided to sell and offered it to us. Without hesitation we paid the number that "balmed his spirit" and we never looked back. It continues to be a treasure that we enjoy seeing every day.

Our friend and colleague Ross Lillie, a recognized expert on the minerals of Southern Illinois, related the following details about the 1988 find. "There were some dozen or so pieces in that find. They were found in a very large pocket some 2-3 meters across and full of brecciated fluorite and water. They were 'face down' in the pocket, so when the miners collected them they had to be careful to lift them up vertically in order to avoid damage to the galenas. It was a one shot deal. No more after that like this. Typical Southern Illinois in that regard. They were sold by the pound mostly with a couple of the best pieces sold individually. Price back then was $1.50-$2.00 pound. In my opinion, this specimen piece is in the top three of the pocket lot." Robert and Stephanie Snyder, Stonetrust.

About the back cover: Two gorgeous rhodochrosite specimens are from the two great locations for these species. The single crystal is from Alma, Park County, Colorado, USA and the cluster of gemmy crystals is from the N'Chwanning II Mine, Kuruman, South Africa. Both specimens are in the collection of Keith and Mauna Proctor.

About the Frontispiece: This is a 28 cm tall crystal cluster of the richest amethyst crystals. Two well-formed, white calcite crystals are on the left margin. In turn, these calcites are overgrown by a younger generation of amethyst geometrically placed on the edges give the calcite a striped appearance. This specimen is from the best source for these, the Santino Mine, Artigas, Uruguay and this specimen is in the Russ Behnke collection.

Acknowledgements

The editor is grateful to Nathaniel King for layout and production assistance. Without his help, this book wouldn't have occurred. Russ Behnke was a significant help in the conceptualization and editing of this book and his always available help is here acknowledged and appreciated. The outside readers/editors are an important, but anonymous resource. Their insight has been invaluable. Janet Nemetz has greatly aided the production of this book and her help was also essential to its production. Joseph J.Pasky and Don Junowich of Cathay Consulting Services were especially kind and solved many issues that the editor was unable to solve.

Table of Contents

Foreword

I love learning about peoples' collections especially when they tell me stories about how they became collectors and show me their collecting choices. *Nature's Garden of Crystals* tells the story of collecting great minerals and crystals. The authors are a veritable *Who's Who Worldwide*; each of whom shares their points of view. Many of the authors are from the USA, but many are from Europe. Among them, they have searched for minerals in most of the world's countries, oftentimes when it was dangerous to do so. When I was young, a single photograph in a book inspired me to learn about minerals. Over the years, many collectors, great or unsung, have told of how a book, a photograph, or an exhibit inspired their lifelong interest in a rewarding hobby. Mineral collecting is the only naturalists' pursuit where collecting is the principal form of conservation.

What is it about collections that captures our imaginations? Let me tell you a short story of a graduate student who collected bullets. His story is one of my long cherished memories. He didn't have a gun to put any of his bullets in. He just loved bullets. He told how technology advanced, patents were infringed, counterfeiters conspired, etc. Most interestingly, wars were almost lost because the early bullets used in India offended religious values. Those bullets were protected from the wet climate by having a thin coating of animal fat and the proscribed method of loading the charge into the gun was to bite off the paper casing so the contents could be loaded into the gun. The collector had rare bullets. There were bullets so rare that even museums did not have examples. There were bullets whose rarity was legendary: six examples known, three examples known. He had a bullet that was unique!

Mineral collecting is as fascinating. Collectors may go into the mountains and find a kind of mineral never before discovered. Currently, this happens in the world about twice a week. It is still possible to find world class crystals yourself, although many collectors find it more rewarding to have a "Silver Pick" to help them when outstanding specimens found by other people become available. Mineral enthusiasts may be doctors, businessmen, engineers, salesmen, teachers, factory workers, woodsmen, farmers, etc. Historically, when farming was one of the principle walks of life, farmers were among the most important mineral collectors, mostly because of their outdoor lives. Mineral collectors usually learn by doing and have no advanced training to aid them. The following chapters cover most of the important mineral collecting specialties and are remarkable because the specimens chosen are so different from each other. The first chapter gives an overview of the variety of minerals, their lore, and the enthusiasm of the chase. Subsequent chapters tell of quests in far away places in order to acquire individually important specimens. Many of the authors tell of their specialties of how a special kind of mineral, minerals from their home areas, or minerals of great beauty have inspired them to be collectors. Some tell of their philosophy of collecting, while two chapters in particular reveal, in breathtaking clarity, how the world of minerals in miniature is exciting. Some authors find beauty in black and white, while others have sought crystals displaying the spectrum of colors. Some of the illustrated crystals are among the best of their kind.

Van King,   Rochester, NY.

Chapter One: *The Keith And Mauna Proctor Family Trust Collection*
by Keith Proctor And Mauna Proctor

The Mauna and Keith Proctor Family Trust Collection has been assembled with the care that a life-long interest in mineral collecting permits. Keith Proctor started mineral collecting in 1947 at the age of ten when his family moved to Idaho Springs, Colorado. Idaho Springs is in the heart of the old Colorado gold and silver mining region, so it was not surprising that Keith wandered around the mine dumps finding crystal specimens and developing an interest in minerals and he began to build a collection of local minerals. In fact, Keith still owns his first "silver pick" specimen, a pyrite that he purchased for fifty dollars.

In 1956 Keith enrolled at the University of Colorado at Boulder, where he received his B.S. degree in chemistry and biology in 1962 and an M.S. degree in molecular biology in 1964. He started collecting seriously shortly after his marriage to Mauna in 1967. His adoration of gem crystals beckoned him to Brazil during the

Mauna and Keith Proctor

1980's and Keith soon wrote four articles on the recent great gem crystal discoveries in Brazil, published by *Gems and Gemology* magazine. Each year readers vote on the most important articles written in that publication. Keith's articles all won awards of excellence. Mr. Proctor has devoted almost all his hobby time to traveling the world to sleuth out fine mineral specimens, and he delights in the choice he has made as he shares their passion for minerals. Through nearly half a century, we have sought fine minerals for our collection. Sometime the travel was to far off countries, as in South America, but we have tried to be where the minerals "are". Our collection has been organized into a trust whereby family members and worthy recipient institutions will benefit from the fruits of our labors. We are temporary custodians of Nature's bounty and soon we hope to find a new home for the specimens you are about to see. Sometime during 2011 or perhaps the following year, these minerals will grace new shelves. It is our hope that our presentation will inspire an ambitious new collector, who will use the entire collection as a platform on which to build their own museum collection. Please contact us. (719) 598-1233 or maunaproctor@aol.com

How would you like to fall in love with the Nature again? We are all captivated by the stunning shapes and colors of flowers, trees, birds, butterflies, or tropical fish. The beauty of minerals mirrors the living world with equally exquisite vitality. There may be a graceful sculpted elegance of a crystal or there may be intensely vivid colors. Every crystal is made up of atoms of one or more elements, the building blocks of the universe. Each crystal shape represents the perfect geometrical form that can result when these elements combined under certain conditions of temperature and pressure, usually deep within the Earth.

We find mineral collecting an awe-inspiring experience. The specimens featured in this book were individually selected as we gained experience and appreciation for a colorful presentation or an artistic shape. No two specimens of the same mineral species, even from a specific location, are exactly the same, although they may have a strong familial resemblance. Crystals contain the "genealogy" of the earth. Their formation may have begun at the dawn of time or may have a more youthful origin of just a few millions of years. Viewing and appreciating a great crystal group is the closest we can ever come to being present at the formation of the world. The intricate and unique design or vivid colors are the result of the creative forces of our planet. Every mineral producing event may be thought of as one of Mother Nature's finest hours.

You don't need any special knowledge to appreciate the rare architecture, color, and beauty of crystals. Seasoned collectors as well as newcomers are inescapably captured by the beauty and symmetry of these extraordinary combinations. An interesting aspect of minerals as a genealogical guide to the earth is that many minerals found in specific mines scattered sparingly throughout every continent of the world, have a distinctiveness whereby an experienced mineral collector may be able to recognize where a specimen originated: such as a specific mine in Namibia, Germany, USA, Brazil, Canada, Italy, and so on.

The following photo galleries, ours as well as the other authors', show exciting collections of gem crystals, gold, silver, and specimens acquired from classic mining locations around the world. The Proctor collection is one of a multitude of premier, privately-owned mineral collections around the world.

There are three basic divisions within our own collection: gem crystal species that could be cut for fine jewelry, the non-gem classic specimens, and crystallized gold, silver and copper specimens from the class of native elements. During his worldwide travels, Mr. Proctor has always sought out the finest representative crystal specimens, not only by visiting active private collections and buying or trading specimens from collectors, dealers, and museum curators, but also by occasionally acquiring specimens directly from the owner of a mine, especially in Brazil. As a result of his mobility, the collection has grown to contain a unique scientific and historical cross-section of many the world's great mines and their best crystal specimens. The gem mineral section alone has over 60 major crystal specimens representing the most historic locations and important finds throughout the world. The gold sub-collection has more than 100 specimens of crystallized gold illustrating 15 major types, habits, and shapes of gold crystals. Many collectors specialize in one or two areas, but sometimes we feel that we must be specializing in diversity. A particularly popular mineral, calcite, is represented by 64 specimens, which for us are absolutely superb. In our second section at the end of the book, we feature these calcite specimens and try to show all of the basic calcite crystal types and shapes. (Collectors often need to be forgiven for their enthusiasms for their "children".)

Over many years, we have also helped find good homes for great mineral specimens. Once in a while something wonderful that we had was the necessary "currency" for a collector who happened to have something that we "needed". We would trade. Sometimes the trades would be very complicated involving numerous specimens. At other times, we would have an opportunity to acquire the "perfect" specimen, but it was part of a large lot recently discovered from a far away mine or was in an old mineral collection for sale. We would then have many more specimens than we needed and oftentimes, we became merchants. There are many opportunities where the collector has to become a seller, as well. The acquisition of minerals can easily outgrow the space allocated for a collection.

In either case, the collector needs to have guidelines. Collectors who have a lifetime of experience know what they want and the places where they can maximize their ability to improve their collections. Some collectors hire professional advisers to guide them, while others develop a rapport with a few trusted mineral dealers. As you may realize, collecting, not just mineral collecting, requires networking, trust, and a plan. Over the years, many collectors have devised a sort of business plan, because collections of all sorts represent a financial resource.

There are 14 criteria we will

One half of the Proctor Collection display area.

by Keith Proctor and Mauna Proctor   2

soon discuss that we have used to help evaluate and determine crystal beauty or what is a great crystal specimen, single crystal, or even a suite of specimens. Some collectors initially have no plan and are simply awe stuck by crystals. As their "taste" in minerals develops, they frequently have to up-grade the specimens they have acquired. We hope that by sharing with you our list of criteria that you may be inspired to build a collection along these lines.

A frequent concern among collectors is the question: "How are top quality crystal specimens valued?" Dr. Pierre Bariand curator (now retired) of the Mineral Collection at the Laboratoire de Minéralogie-Cristalographie, Université Pierre et Marie Curie (Sorbonne), one of the most prestigious European museums said... "It is difficult to value specimens of the highest quality because the mines they came from are closed so these specimens cannot be replaced, and so they are priceless. It is much like evaluating a Monet or Renoir painting." Nonetheless, we must start from a set of principles in order to reach a goal of getting truly fine minerals specimens as opposed to mere examples of a specimen.

We will use vignettes of the larger images in our main photo gallery to illustrate our points. What are the determining artistic factors, which produce a great crystal specimen and arouse our sense of appreciation and awe? We mentioned that trees, flowers, birds, butterflies, and tropical fish, have standards of beauty, desirability, etc., but when one gets serious about studying and collecting within these otherwise familiar fields, it soon becomes apparent that a particular lily has more significance to the gardener than many others which seem just about as beautiful.

Our list of criteria focuses on building a truly fine mineral collection, but the principles are valid for anyone wishing to build even a modest collection. We mentioned that minerals also represent a financial resource. Again, we want to emphasize that someday, your mineral collection will become someone else's property. You will want your family to get as much benefit from your efforts as possible. Collecting, then, is also a form of investment and in any form of investment; the investor also looks toward resale potential. In selecting and investing in world-class crystal specimens we need to evaluate and understand those traits that distinguish truly superior specimens of their species. In assembling a world-class crystal collection, the aesthetics of what constitutes beauty, what are the standards of perfection, and especially what has investment value are important factors to keep in mind. These factors are useful no matter what price range specimens fall into.

Our Fourteen Criteria for Judging Beauty
and Selecting Superior Crystal Specimens

Price Levels Of Specimens: Most of these 14 criteria for judging and determining quality and beauty apply to all price levels and all sizes of collector specimens. They apply to $200 specimens as well as $200,000 or $2 million dollar museum quality specimens. The vignettes for examples are more fully described and labeled in the photo gallery.

Size Considerations: Although we didn't explicitly place this concept in our 14 points, large specimen size, when all otherfactors are optimal usually equals dramatically large price premiums for a specimen. It is extremely difficult to find a specimen 12-18" across (such as the quartz fish) that has the perfection of a miniature-sized specimen, and these also should be marveled over and highly valued. We will frequently discuss the interplay of several criteria in our list.

1.   Desirable Color: Desirable color is the first criterion to consider when selecting superior specimens. When choosing our specimens, we place great emphasis on selecting the most vivid colors that each species might possess, or that each mine or discovery was famous for. For example, the Red Cloud mine wulfenites are a standard of excellent red color in the species. The exceedingly bright yellow wulfenite crystals from the Santa Eulalia, Mexico mines are another example of a locality setting a standard for a particular color. Muddy or cloudy colors should be avoided when searching for investment quality minerals. Example is wulfenite.

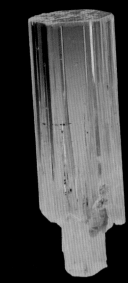

2. Gemmy Crystals: Gem crystals look as though they could cut at least one genuine flawless gemstone. Crystals with transparent areas, but are full of flaws are said to be gemmy. Gem crystals (beryl, tourmaline, etc.) and gemmy crystal species like wulfenite display many of the qualities of cut gemstones. The transparency or, at least the translucency, of crystals is an extremely important factor of beauty and value, just as with traditional cut gemstones. The shapes of most gemmy crystals - at their best - have great architectural lines. Some collectors will buy a pretty tourmaline or beryl crystal just because it is on some kind of matrix. That is okay for reference collectors, but an ordinary specimen is not an investment piece. Most of the best multicolored gem tourmaline crystals are of necessity off matrix, while those on matrix need certain attributes. Example is aquamarine.

3. Luster on Crystal Faces: The degree of light reflection from crystal faces is important. A mineral that ideally should have glassy, mirror-like finishes must have this property when considering a specimen for its investment value. Some crystals have an internal radiance supplementing the external appearance of a specimen. The sheen and even shimmer of these natural crystal facets reflects not only the play of light on their external and internal structure, but also the favorable growth conditions that formed them eons ago. Crystal faces are natural consequences of the regular arrangement of the chemical constituents of a mineral. We are very fond of the rhodochrosite shown on the back cover and the tanzanite seen in chapter one, as their luster is magnificent. With well-chosen lighting, the entire gemmy or translucent crystal may possess beautiful luminescence, which along with its sharp faces contribute greatly to its beauty. Some crystals appear to glow with their own internal light without special studio lights. Example is tanzanite.

4. Common vs. Rare Crystal Types: Many specimens are desirable and become famous because their crystals exhibit a shape either classically typical of the species (such as a statuesque, tall and gemmy aquamarine) or rare (such as a very flat hexagonal morganite beryl crystal). Many people collect entire suites of specimens of the same species (such as pyromorphite or wulfenite) because each specimen illustrates the great variety of crystal shapes and variety of colors known to that species. We have sub-collections of these and other species including tourmaline, beryl, topaz, kunzite, tanzanite, garnet, and crystallized gold. Example is gold.

5. Total Composition: The total composition of the specimen is of major significance. Crystals still attached to their host rock are highly sought after, and the importance of the overall aesthetic arrangement or composition of these crystals on the matrix cannot be overestimated. The crystals can easily appear to be misplaced and thus the specimen can seem "out of balance" as opposed to a crystal arrangement that demonstrates harmony, balance, and even a certain "rhythm". (Collectors sometimes lament: "The specimen would look beautiful if only the main crystal were in a different

place.) If all other factors are equal, two or more crystals flaring off the host rock are more interesting than just one (such as if they are in a V-shape). Ideally, there should be dramatic relief between the crystals and matrix. Crystals lying flat on the matrix are far less interesting than those "standing" up. If there is no host rock, then a cluster of radiating crystals is generally better than just one crystal. Thousands of specimens have been trimmed to get the "perfect" composition. This is where your eye and creativity comes into play. Innumerable masterpiece specimens have been created this way, greatly increasing the original value paid by a large factor. Note: Trimming is an art in itself. While there may be great reward, there may also be loss. The specimen may be ruined from unexpected breakage or the hoped for proportions may not be achieved, as matrix does not always "behave".

Sometimes a splendid artistic composition or arrangement needs an asymmetrical counterpoint to establish a tension or relationship between the component crystals and patterns. A large crystal with a uniquely canted companion crystal may be especially lovely. The best painters and sculptors throughout history have used dramatic tension and asymmetry to add interest and to create a more intense focus on the subject of their composition. Mineral specimens may have this property by chance and it is important to recognize the relationship crystals on a specimen have to each other. In selecting superb crystal specimens the tension may be so subtle for some people that a great specimen may not be among the first ones chosen bysome dealers or some collectors. Be prepared for "Aha" moments. We recommend that collectors spend some time evaluating a specimen for its compositional factors. A well-chosen artistic specimen will be a delight in a collection. There are many specimens to choose from in this book. We hope that you will see many of the aesthetic qualities that we see in these.

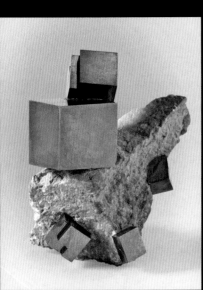

6. The Focal Point(S): A specimen that possesses (or lacks) a major focal point is another vital component of composition. What does our eye tend to fall on and what rivets our attention as we view a specimen? The focal point should be a major crystal or crystals or a beautiful feature that stands out. A jumbled mass of crystals of all the same small size - with no focal point - may not be what we want as an investment. Many major collectors believe that a specimen with crystals flaring from the horizon is highly desirable. Others believe a 360° view with perfection all around is the ultimate group they must have. Such a specimen would have no preferred "front" or "back". It would be displayable on all "sides". The focal point could also be the position that shows the tension factor mentioned earlier. Remember that minerals really are able to be evaluated in artistic terms. Most major collectors are very fastidious about the artistic qualities of a specimen and, for this reason alone, aesthetic mineral specimens invariably bring high prices. We, again, invite you to examine all of the photo galleries in this book for the artistic merits you see. Example is pyrite.

7. Perfection of Crystals And Matrix: The overall perfection of crystals and matrix is a critical consideration. If major crystals are buried partially, or are encumbered by the matrix, or are laying flat, they are often a major distraction from the beauty of the specimen. Additionally, just as with any work of art, the beauty and perfection would be disrupted by any significant blemish that our eyes invariably see. However, our eyes take great delight in looking at the harmony, rhythm, unity, and balance of a perfect crystal composition. Jack Halpern, a California collector, said that "Dings Deliver Demerits". Universally, collectors acknowledge this point. Centrally located, obviously broken or missing crystals often spell the kiss of death for effective reselling. Matrix may also show undesirable features. Artistic trimming of the specimen may save the day, however. The very pinnacles of crystal perfection are those specimens, which are known for not having nicks on them. Wulfenite and azurite are examples of minerals that are difficult to find without some small bit of damage. Collectors of the highest grade of minerals often use magnifiers to detect the slightest amount of damage. Glass and porcelain antiques have a similar standard of needing to be damage-free in order to command the highest prices. Example is sulphur.

8. Size Ratio: The size ratio between the crystal or crystal group affects appreciation of the overall form, composition, eye-appeal, beauty and, therefore, retail value. A crystal or group of crystals attached to a matrix should approach perfect composition and be in harmony with the matrix size. When crystals are on too tiny or too large a matrix, the size ratio will seem "wrong". Ideally, the crystals must visually counterbalance the matrix. Many specimens fall far short in this major criterion of specimen and crystal artistry, because their crystals or matrix are relatively too large or too small. However, literally thousands of specimens have been trimmed to meet a higher artistic standard. Many of our specimens have had unwanted material removed by professional trimmers so that the resultant specimen has a pleasing effect. Example is amethyst.

9. Color Contrast: The color contrast between the crystal(s) and its matrix should ideally be intense, such as with the red rubies on white matrix, vivid green emeralds on black or white matrix, green gemmy demantoid garnet crystals that grew on white calcite or quartz crystals, or red vanadinites sprinkled over white bladed barite crystals. The matrix and associated minerals can give a stunning visual effect. We emphasize that color contrast is a very important trait that can be a definitive factor determining beauty in many great specimens. Black minerals on black backgrounds may be beautiful if their luster is contrasting, but even red on red may be undesirable. Example is mimetite.

10. Isolated Crystals: With some exceptions, isolated crystals on the host rock are more attractive and interesting than those crystals tightly clumped together. When crystals are isolated, they are easier to study as it is then easier to see their various crystal forms. The isolated yellow/green mimetite crystals from the Elura mine in Australia in our gallery pop out at the viewer. This color splash offered by isolated colorful crystals might govern our decision to acquire them. The Chinese realgar in our gallery is a crystal that is irresistible for the collector looking for an isolated crystal with a variety of well-met criteria: color, perfection, transparency, etc. Example is calcite.

11. Rarity: Rarity has many aspects. A given species may be rare. A mineral may be rarely seen in crystals or may rarely have a certain color. Rare crystal shape or an unexpectedly unusual mineral association can be the Surprise Factor important in determining desirability and value.

There are more than 2,000 species of minerals that form visible crystals, but far fewer than 200 form beautiful crystal specimens often enough that a collector could hope to own them. Rarity has another half to its story. Aesop's Fables taught that "familiarity breeds contempt". Many collectors frequently avoid the common minerals, quartz, feldspar, mica, etc., partly because they are common and they generally have few good-looking specimens. For this reason, a great, but white feldspar crystal might sell for a fraction of the amount a pretty mineral would bring. Similarly, the best specimen in the world of an unattractive mineral probably would not be as high-priced as an above average quality beautiful mineral specimen of a common mineral.

Ideally rare species should also be beautiful in color and composition, such as the two ruby crystals on a white marble matrix in this collection. Although ruby and emerald are not as rare as truly rare minerals, but still there are few of them. In all fine crystal specimens the rarity of their quality and composition as well as the rarity and miracle of their creation and the great odds against their survival, make collectors marvel and they will want to own them as objects d'art in their own right. Example is brookite.

12.   Resembling Familiar Objects: Often, a specimen that resembles some familiar object is highly prized by the buyer or viewer. The familiarity of these "look-alike" crystal specimens is fun and they strike a responsive chord in the mind and eye of the viewer, which in turn repeatedly increases their enjoyment of the piece. Our best example of mimicry is a smoky quartz perfect fish. We've suspected that someday a great fishing executive or famous sports fisherman would have to have one of our specimens. It is what people have called: the *World's Greatest Stone Fish.* For mimicry, it has no equal. In Asia, natural stone mimics have sold to appreciators of nature's art for millions of dollars. We have noted many examples of imitation or mimicry in our photo gallery. Example is the Stone Fish.

13.   Collecting In Suites: Collecting In Suites: Collectors soon begin to specialize in objects they like. Specialization is common in antique collecting or collecting stamps, coins, or automobiles. Mineral collectors collect tourmaline, beryls, calcite, gold, azurite, wulfenite, etc. and these sub-collections are called "suites". Some collectors seek only certain mineral colors, including one person we know who collects only purple minerals! There are collections of single crystals, twin crystals, minerals all from one chemical class such as native elements or carbonates, mineral from their home state or a favorite faraway place. A well-chosen specialized group of specimens may be more valuable than their individual specimens, because the effort and time re-

quired to assemble a collection also represents a rare opportunity. Good minerals usually cannot be ordered on demand. Example is tourmaline.

14.   The 28 Most Expensive Species: Price Considerations In Investing: The last criterion for selecting fine specimens concerns the eventual resale of the specimen for a profit. You must know what species easily sell. Most of the consistently highest prices paid for minerals have been for about only 28 species. The top fourteen species are listed in a chart in descending order of dollars spent by collectors for the "top" specimens. The remaining 14 species are in no specific order of highest prices paid. There may be many variations in this ranking, but the list should be a guide for anyone wanting to know which species have commanded the highest prices.

Very simply, if we are buying with the hope to eventually sell our specimens for a profit, or at least easily recover their cost, then the proverbial supply and demand equation reigns supreme. Buy what people want. If you are a dyed-in-the-wool mineral collector who has no need to consider ultimate value, then buy what YOU want. In reality, many specimens are irresistable and price is not a factor - big or small. Sometimes paying "too much" is more important than letting a specimen or collection "get away". Nonetheless, the price of acquiring fine things is a conscious choice.

These 28 top mineral species are extremely popular, and there are hundreds and even thousands of buyers who want to acquire the best examples of these 28 species. If we must intentionally buy wisely, we must consider resale value. Without a doubt these 28 listed species are the safest bet. As always, with low supply there is safety in the high demand species and the number of buyers. When you see a collage of some of the top species, you begin to see why they are the ones to have.

Over a lifetime of mineral acquisition, we have generally adhered to the 14 criteria of what makes a great mineral specimen as well as to what makes an important mineral collection. We hope that you agree and enjoy the minerals we have to offer. Part of our intention in presenting the discussion and images has been to advertise what we believe to be a unique and desirable concentration of quality minerals. Because of the effort involved in assembling our collection, we believe that it is worth preservation as a unit. There are mineral masterpieces and one-of-a-kind specimens in the collection that someone might enjoy for themselves or share with many as an instant quality museum collection.

Collectors are the preservers of man's and nature's finest artistic works; without them, many museums would not exist. The Proctor collection affords an outstanding opportunity to obtain a great collection or for someone to be a philanthropist who wishes to preserve a legacy of beauty and history. As you study this pictorial inventory of the Proctor collection in this wonderful book, which features many superb collections of the world's great collectors, we invite you to join us in falling in love with Nature, again.

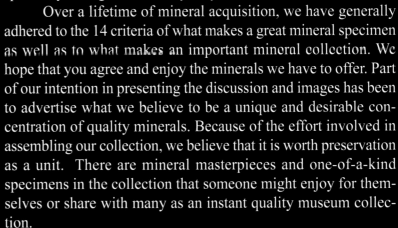

by Keith Proctor and Mauna Proctor   8

Top 28 Species

1. Rhodochrosite
2. Gem Tourmalines
3. Beryl varieties: Aquamarine, Emerald, Morganite, Heliodor, Red Beryls
4. Gold
5. Tanzanite
6. Silver
7. Topaz (especially blue)
8. Azurite (Tsumeb)
9. Stibnite (China)
10. Dioptase (Tsumeb)
11. Fluorite
12. Pyromorphite
13. Kunzite
14. Quartz
15. Calcite
16. Apophyllite (only green)
17. Cerussite (Tsumeb)
18. Smithsonite
19. Mimetite
20. Adamite
21. Vanadinite
22. Wulfenite
23. Crocoite
24. Scheelite
25. Apatite
26. Corundum: Ruby
27. Amazonite (Colorado)
28. Copper

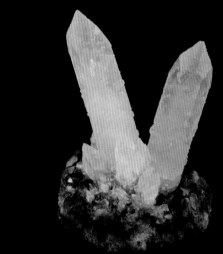

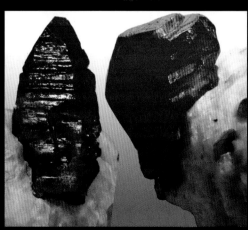

The Gem Silicate Family
Species That Are Cut For Jewelry: Tourmaline, Beryl, Topaz, Kunzite, Tanzanite, and Garnet

Tourmaline is unique among all of the cuttable gem species, because of the wide variety of colors it may have. Elbaite contains sodium, aluminum, and lithium as important elements and when pure is colorless, but trace elements can dramatically change the color. (e.g. Iron with both $^{2+}$ and $^{3+}$ valences may produce various shades of green and blue). Manganese in the absence of much iron produces pinks or reds. Copper can produce the "electric blues and greens" of so-called Paraiba-color tourmaline. The black schorl tourmaline is iron-rich and contains little or no lithium. In fact, almost all gem cuttable and colorful tourmalines contain essential or dominant lithium. The rare tourmaline olenite is an exception.

Tourmaline
Blue And Red Crystal
Barra de Salinas,
Minas Gerais (M.G.), Brazil

This beautiful tourmaline has the rare color combination: blue with red. This specimen came from the Mark Weill collection. The crystal is 8.9 cm tall and 5 cm wide and was pictured in Marc Weill's supplement to the *Mineralogical Record,* January-February 2008, page 52. This multicolored gem tourmaline epitomizes why Brazil is called "The Paradise of Gems". Jeff Scovil photograph.

Rubellite Tourmaline, Alto Ligonha, Mozambique. (right) The Alta Ligonha concessions in Mozambique produced their beautiful red (rubellite) gem tourmalines almost fifty years ago. We are particularly fond of this gem crystal. It measures 3.3 cm wide and 7 cm long.
Harold and Erika Van Pelt photograph.

Rubellite Tourmaline, Jos, Nigeria. (left) This is a nice gem rubellite crystal. Specimen measures 5.7 by 2.2 cm.
Jeff Scovil photograph.

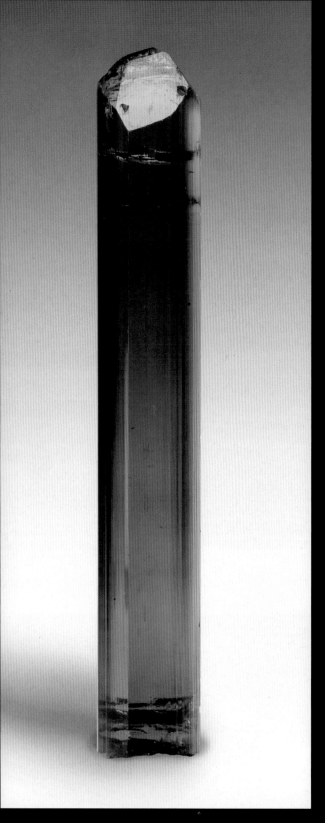

Tourmaline, Sapo Mine, M.G. Brazil. Multicolored tourmalines are always a joy to look at. This crystal has interesting color patterns. It has both, so-called, polychrome and watermelon color zoning. This four-color crystal is 12 cm long, including the fibrous end. The smaller crystal on this crystal group shows an exposed bright red core and has a thin green exterior reminding one of a watermelon. The principal crystal also has a visible red shaft and above that is a thin band of pale yellow/green tourmaline. Near the top of the crystal is a thin zone of pale blue-green grading in a layer of dark blue, so-called, indicolite, and then it has a dark purple cap with a glassy top. The tourmaline-forming solutions obviously changed composition several times producing this fine crystal. The blue fibrous bottom of this long crystal gives a clue about how this crystal formed.
Joe Budd photograph.

Tourmaline, Pederneira Mine, Minas Gerais, Brazil. The famous Pederneira mine is noted for producing gem green tourmaline specimens. This nearly flawless crystal is 9.5 cm long. Many collectors collect both cut gemstones and natural crystals of the same color into so-called "Rough and Cut collections". Joe Budd photograph.

Tourmaline, Cruzeiro Mine, M. G., Brazil. (Crystal on the right). In April 1994, a few pockets of tricolor, gemmy tourmaline (green on the bottom, colorless in the center [achroite], and hot pink on the top) were found at the Cruzeiro (Cross) mine. This 10.8 cm long gem crystal was found then. Near the top there is a thick, colorless layer of tourmaline, called achroite, between the top red layer and the bottom green layer. This colorless layer indicates that there was a growth period, when neither iron nor manganese were significantly available, in the tourmaline-forming solution to create color. The geochemists have no sure idea how fast these gem crystals grew, although they generally agree that they formed "fast", probably on the order of days or weeks. If we are observant, we can usually see that each crystal has its own story of formation to tell and is often characteristic of a locality. Joe Budd photograph.

Tourmaline, Barra de Salinas Mine, Brazil. (Crystal in the center) The world famous Barra (pronounced Baha) de Salinas mine in Brazil produced this beautiful tri-color crystal in the 1980s. This 9.5 cm long crystal has a very pleasing and subtle color generally grading from one color to another instead of having sharp lines of demarcation. Acquired from the Dr. Steve Smale collection. Joe Budd photograph.

Tourmaline, Morro Redondo (Round Mountain) Mine, Brazil. (Crystal on the left) In the late 1980s, a big find of bi-color tourmalines, pink with green tips, was made at the small Morro (pronounced Moho) Redondo mine. The specimen has a very thin achroite layer between the green and rose-colored layers. This 6.6 cm long tri-color crystal was acquired from the Dr. Steve Smale collection. Joe Budd photograph.

Tourmaline, Cruzeiro Mine, Brazil. These three crystals come from the October 1996 find at the Cruzerio Mine, the world's largest tourmaline mine. These three crystals show why tourmaline is sometimes called the "Rainbow Stone".

First Crystal (left side). This 8.9 cm long, five-color crystal starts with red on the bottom, then goes to green, to a good pink section, to a thin band of green, and finishing with a red top. The tourmaline-forming solutions that formed this crystal changed composition several times. Manganese causes the reds and pinks and Iron (Fe^{2+}, and Fe^{3+}) causes the green and blue colors.

Second Crystal: (middle) This is an interesting 6.4 cm long gemmy crystal. It has a vertical red streak running up the crystal's left side. If tourmalines are color banded, they usually have horizontal banding and not vertical stripes as seen here. This crystal goes from red (on the left side) and green on the base (on the right side), grading into a red top. Acquired from the Dr. Steve Smale collection.

Third Crystal (right side) This is a double gem crystal (7 cm long) with a green base, moving up to pink, then to a narrow green band, and finally finishing with a red top. The color scheme is certainly unusual. Acquired from the Stuart Wilensky collection. Group photograph by Joe Budd.

Multicolored Tourmalines on an Albite Matrix, Pederneira Mine, Brazil. Multicolored tourmaline crystals on matrix are desirable and one which displays watermelon-color zoning is very desirable. The crystals create a masterpiece of composition, displaying pink bases grading into a delicate green with pink tips. It is unusual that the back right crystal is so different in color pattern from the others in the group. Specimen measures 17.8 cm tall by 9.5 cm wide. Jeff

Tourmaline on Quartz Crystals, Pederneira Mine, Brazil. (above) The gemminess and perfection of these tourmalines on the quartz crystals is very attractive. Specimen measures 20 cm tall, 16.5 cm wide with the longest tourmaline crystal being 14 cm long. Jeff Scovil photograph.

Tourmaline "Pencil" Crystals on Quartz, Escondido Mine, M.G., Brazil. (left) These tourmalines on matrix are on a 7.5 cm tall milky quartz crystal, surrounded by smaller quartzes and projecting out from this crystal cluster are ten, thin, "pencil" tourmalines. The gemmy terminated crystals are 5 cm long and some are doubly terminated. Found circa 1997. Joe Budd photograph.

Tourmaline, Paprok Area, Afghanistan. Paprok is famous for producing single crystals of tourmalines and specimens with a small amount of matrix. We were privileged to be present when this specimen reached the marketplace. It has many qualities searched for in a mineral specimen. The largest tourmaline crystal is sharp, colorful, and well-placed and there are accessory minerals that compliment the specimen. The smoky quartz is on the opposite end of the specimen and is nearly as large as the tourmalines. Three small colorful tourmalines are positioned on the front edge and are partly surrounded by "cauliflowers" of cleavelandite feldspar. The color zoning is particularly appealing. The yellow green to grass green layers are strong and vibrant as are the pink prisms. The white cleavelandite variety of albite is literally the "icing of the cake". Specimen measures 15.2 cm wide by 14 cm tall. Jeff Scovil photograph.

Cinnamon Colored Tourmaline on Tourmaline Crystals, Coronel Murta, M.G., Brazil. We see here a small masterpiece of the gem kingdom. Several prominent tourmaline spires with color zoning including the unusual cinnamon color rise up from a bed of horizontal gem tourmaline crystals accented by light purple lepidolite mica. Note the rare yellow color in some of the tourmaline crystals. Specimen measures 10 by 13.3 cm. James Elliott photograph.

Tourmaline, Pederneira Mine, M.G., Brazil. (above right) Combination pieces are always desirable. The gemmy green and blue tourmaline on the right is associated with a red and green tourmaline on the left. In side view, the red and green tourmaline looks as though it is a banded bi-color crystal, but the red zone is surrounded by a green sheath, in watermelon fashion. Specimen measures 8.3 cm long by 4.1 cm wide. Jeff Scovil photograph.

Schorl Tourmaline (Black) – Erongo Mountains, Namibia. Schorl is actually quite uncommon in good crystals, although it is the most common kind of tourmaline. Even in the Erongo Mountains, collectors and miners are constantly searching for pockets in hopes of getting good schorl crystals. They usually find single crystals, sometimes with some matrix. This group with a "V"-shape is nice. Specimen measures 7.5 cm high by 6.4 cm wide. Jeff Scovil photograph.

Tourmaline Altered to Pink Lepidolite Mica, Pederneira Mine, M. G., Brazil. Some of the surface of these tourmalines dissolved away and the tourmaline that was underneath completely altered, nearly 400 million years ago, to pink lepidolite mica. Adding to the uniqueness of the specimen is a "fresh" double terminated quartz crystal on the front face. Technically, this specimen should be called a lepidolite mica pseudomorph after tourmaline. Specimen measures 6.4 cm tall by 3.8 cm wide. Joe Budd photograph.

Rubellite from Mogok District, Myan Mar. This tourmaline shows dark red rubellite tips resting on medium red prisms. Specimen (left) measures 15.2 cm wide by 8.3 cm deep. Jeff Scovil photograph.

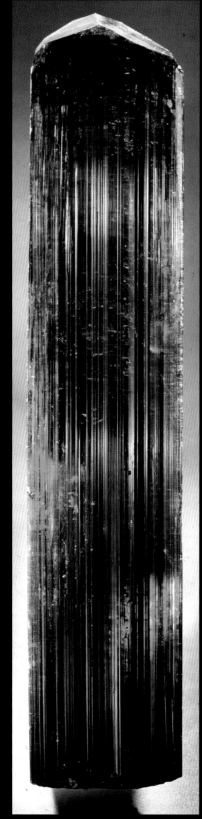

Emerald Green Tourmaline, Virgem da Lapa, M. G., Brazil. (left) This enormous tourmaline crystal (2400 grams/ 12,000 carats.) was found at the Xanda/Limoneiro mining complex about 1976. With back-lighting, it is translucent, showing many delightful gemmy areas. It measures 33 cm long and 7 cm inches wide. The crystal is in pristine condition.

The Proctors gave this masterpiece crystal to Brigham Young University geology department in 2005 and now the University intends to sell the specimen to raise scholarship money to help students from disadvantaged families to go to college. This tourmaline is certainly one of the best, huge, single, green tourmaline crystals in any museum or private collection.

This photograph does not adequately portray the beauty, gemminess, and color of this magnificent crystal. Overall, the crystal is actually more emerald green (as seen through the lighter colored crystal's base on the right side and the middle left crystal edges). The crystal is so thick it needs bright lights, though. With this crystal directly in front of three vertical halogen lights, it is stunningly beautiful as it lights up like a Christmas tree bulb.
Harold and Erica Van Pelt photograph.

Tourmaline, Virgem da Lapa, M. G., Brazil. (above) This is a mammoth three color, gem tourmaline crystal. It has a delicate pink tip and then grades into a pleasing and subtle blue and the remainder of the magnificent gemmy green section is cuttable. The crystal is doubly terminated. It measures 40.6 cm long and 2.5 cm wide. It was discovered about 1976 at either the Limoneiro or Xanda (pronounced Shanda) Mine, near the city of Virgem da Lapa (Virgin of the Cave), Minas Gerais (meaning General Mines), Brazil. Brazil is well-known for its high standards of cuttable tourmalines. Many of the long gem tourmaline crystals were handled roughly by careless *garimpeiros* (miners), who believed that large individual gem crystals would never find buyers. Large gem crystals often were immediately faceted at a cutting operation near the mine site. This huge gem crystal was saved because it passed through the hands of three crystal lovers and collectors – not through gem brokers.
Joe Budd photograph.

Beryl: Aquamarine, Heliodor, and Emerald

Aquamarine Variety of Beryl, Jaquito Mine, Bahia State, Brazil. This is a beautiful, doubly-terminated, gem, aquamarine crystal that was found in the early 1980s. It has wonderful vertical surface texturing showing etched or dissolution marks. This texture developed during the formation of this crystal millions of years ago, when it went back and forth, in and out of solution. This specimen measures 10 cm long and 3 cm wide. Jeff Scovil photograph.

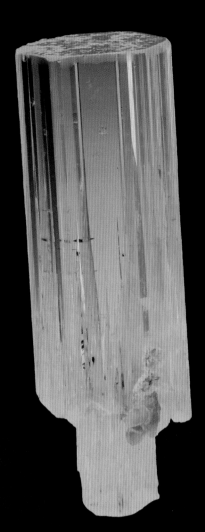

Aquamarine Variety of Beryl. Shigar Valley, Pakistan. Pictured here is a sceptered aquamarine. It is 7.5 cm long by 3.8 cm wide. This crystal is a true scepter, because the entire overhang of the top part of this crystal, where the lower stalk meets the larger part, is completely terminated and the small stalk is also completely terminated.
Joe Budd photograph.

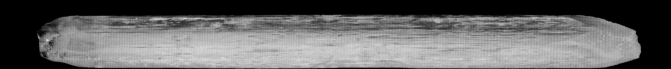

Aquamarine Variety of Beryl, "Pencil", Jaquito Mine. This elongated, exceptionally thin, aquamarine is a very unusual crystal. During the early 1980s only a few of these, so-called, "pencils" were found in this remarkable mine. This doubly-terminated crystal measures 18.4 cm long by 1.7 cm wide. Acquired from the Jim Minette collection.
Joe Budd photograph.

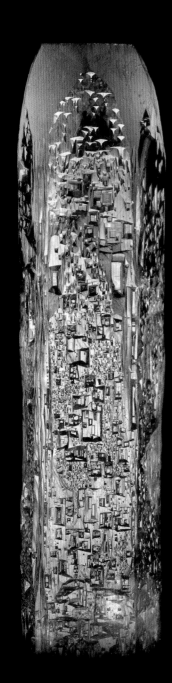

Aquamarine variety of Beryl, Angicos Mine, Medina, M.G., Brazil. This crystal is noted for its size, deep teal color, and for its distinctive surface texture. At 27.9 cm long by 6.1 cm wide and weighing 1771 grams. (8855 carats), this gem crystal is enormous. It is also famous because it was one of the three Angicos mine aquamarine crystals on the front cover of the *Mineralogical Record,* volume 4, 2002. Like the surfaces on the Jaquito Mine and Volodarsk beryls in our photo gallery, the surface texturing seen on these crystals resulted as they were partially dissolved during formation. Much of this blue-green crystal is gem material. It has a *c*-face on top, with six, 5 cm high and very wide, 2nd order "pyramid" faces progressing and tapering down from the top. This crystal was found in early 1997. Keith visited the mine shortly after the discovery the same year, and with his interpreter, he interviewed the still excited mine owner. This interview is cited here. Most Brazilian miners and experts agree that this aquamarine discovery was the most important of the previous 30 years. Very few fine crystals were retrieved and most were considerably smaller. Most of the production was sent to the gem cutters.

The Story of the Discovery of the Angicos Mine Aquamarines - by Steve Voynick - *Rock And Gem* – March, 2000.

"Since very few mine owners could assume the tremendous costs and increased risks of hard rock mining, the supply of fine Brazilian gem-crystal specimens began to decline sharply in the 1970s.

"Nevertheless, miners still occasionally make great Hard Rock discoveries. On May 20, 1997, hard rock miners in the Angicos mine (near Medina city) blasted into a spectacular Aquamarine occurrence. The bottom of the large, oval-shaped pocket was covered with fine crystals of black biotite Mica and pink lepidolite Mica. Lying atop the two types of mica were 40 aquamarine crystals. All were loose and isolated, that is, not attached to matrix. Half were superb gem-quality collector specimens. Five crystals, including one nearly 12 inches in length (pictured here as one of the darkest blue colors), ranked among the world's best.

"Two months later, a few of the smaller aqua specimens showed up in the U.S. When Keith Proctor heard of this Aquamarine find, he immediately telephoned his Brazilian contacts. 'They confirmed that the aquamarine discovery was the biggest in 30 years,' Keith recounts, 'and that the best crystals were still in Brazil. I flew to Brazil the next day. Two days later, I had tracked down and purchased three of the best crystals—most were doubly terminated and superb gem quality.'

"Interestingly, the supernatural may have played a role in that discovery. The Angicos mine, and its owner. had fallen on hard times and had been about to close. Ten months before this Aquamarine discovery, the mine owner was trapped and almost killed in an underground cave-in. Three months later; a miner was killed in a fight. Then a deluge of rain flooded the workings. The mine probably would have closed then, except a stranger (whom the new owner had never met) gave him 900 feet of hose, free of charge, enabling him to pump out the mine.

"Just before the almost fatal cave-in, the mine owner had dreamed about a pocket of Aquamarine crystals that had teased him and 'talked' to him, saying 'we have been here for many years', and they demanded to know 'why are you disturbing us?' Then, 10 days before the discovery, the same crystals spoke to him again in a second dream, this time informing him that he was driving his drift (tunnel) in the wrong direction, and that if he shifted his direction 1 meter to the right, 'his life would be realized.' He altered the direction of the drift, and 10 days later blasted into this spectacular, iconic Aquamarine pocket!" Jeff Scovil photograph.

Aquamarine Variety of Beryl. Angicos Mine, Medina City, M.G., Brazil. The size (24 x 4.4 cm and 735 grams / 3700 carats), gemminess, and surface texturing on this world-class aquamarine are stunning. It is also interesting that the two views (A and B) of this crystal are so different. It took heavy bargaining and two long trips to accomplish the trade for this breath-taking crystal. The top 2/3 of this crystal is totally gem and it, too, has a marvelous surface texture. (This crystal is not as dark blue as shown in view B, but has a more pleasing darker blue green, teal color than seen in view A.) Jeff Scovil photographs.

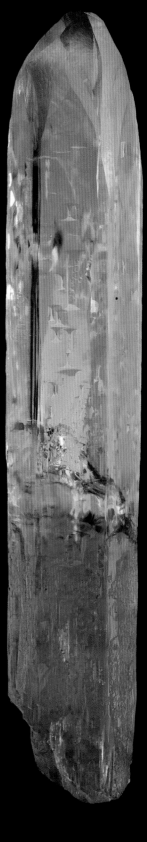

Mr. Proctor went to Brazil in August 1997 - shortly after this momentous aquamarine discovery to try to ferret out a couple of these once-in-a-lifetime specimens for his museum collection. He interviewed the mine owner at length (see previous page) and this photo shows him sitting inside the gem pocket cavity at the Angicos Mine.

View A   View B

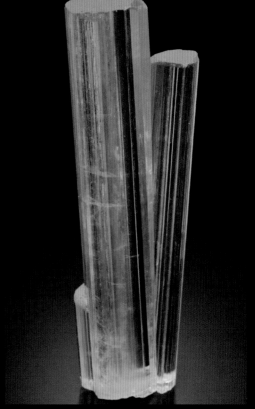

Aquamarine Variety of Beryl on Schorl and Feldspar, Erongo Mountains, Namibia. The process of mining these crystals is laborious. It is mostly hand-work in solid granite. These doubly terminated aquamarines on matrix are very uncommon and highly sought after. Specimen measures 8.9 x 6.4 cm. The longest crystal is 5.7 cm. Lynn Sim photograph.

Aquamarine Variety of Beryl, Shigar Valley, Pakistan. Seen here are two intergrown, 8.9 long aquamarine crystals. The two tips act almost like fiber optic tubes and are a much darker blue looking from the top rather than the side. Jeff Scovil photograph.

Morganite Variety of Beryl and Kunzite Variety of Spodumene, Nuristan, Afghanistan. This is an unusual combination of species. Interestingly, they are both colored slightly differently by a trace of manganese. On the left side is a 7.5 cm morganite crystal and a 2.5 cm pink/purple kunzite crystal on the right. Specimen measures 14 by 10.2 cm. Jeff Scovil photograph.

View A   View B   Heliodor

Heliodor Variety of Beryl, Mine #6, Volodarsk, Ukraine. This wonderful yellow green to yellow beryl (called heliodor) was found at an excellent locality for gem beryls in the Ukraine, formerly a province of Union of Soviet Socialists Republic. Two mines there produced most of the heliodors. Mine #2 produced the more familiar and less perfect, irregularly shaped and highly dissolution "etched" heliodor beryls that were occasionally seen on the market for the last four decades. However, Mine #6 produced better crystals, but also indented with dissolution faces. These either came out of hiding recently or were perhaps from a recent chance discovery. These very gemmy crystals have subtle surface texturing that makes them highly desirable and rank among some of the finest heliodor beryls ever mined. The 400 gram (2000 carat) crystal on the left is 13.3 cm long by 4.4 wide. View A shows the stunning surface texturing, while a second view (B) of the same crystal shows its gemminess. Left (A) is a Joe Budd photograph while center image (B) is by Jeff Scovil.

Heliodor Variety of Beryl, Mine #6, Volodarsk, Ukraine. (upper right) The yellow heliodor on the far right has a much better color and is exactly the same length as the previous specimen (View A and B) making a beautiful matched pair. In the gem business, if they find a pale yellow or green crystal, they gently heat the clean, cut stones and produce the more valuable blue aquamarine color. This specimen is a rare "survivor". Specimen measures 13.3 cm long. Right image is by Jeff Scovil.

View A

View B

Heliodor Variety of Beryl, Mine #6, Volodarsk-Volynskii, Ukraine. This third Heliodor gem crystal, with its architecture and sharp surface texturing and transparency, has dramatic dissolution surface texturing which is equally beautiful to the two previous Volodarsk crystals. This crystal measures only 10.8 cm long by 4.2 cm wide and weighs 254 grams (1270 carats). Keith acquired this specimen from the Ernie Schlichter collection. As we see these two views (A and B) of the same specimen under different lighting conditions, it becomes obvious that during formation, this smaller crystal, like the other, went back and forth, into and out of solution. The stunning surface produced in this way is a natural work of art. View B of the crystal is very gemmy appearing by transmitted light, while reflections in View A emphasizes the surface texture. Joe Budd photographs.

Heliodor Variety of Beryl, Tajikistan. (below and lower left) This is a Heliodor Beryl from the Yellow Water mine in the Pamir Mountains in Tajikistan. It displays a rare screw-like spiral - a so-called helix inclusion. In 40 years of collecting the Proctors have seen only four spiral inclusions in beryls like this. How these spirals were formed is a mystery. Specimen measures 4.8 x 1.23 cm. Van King photographs.

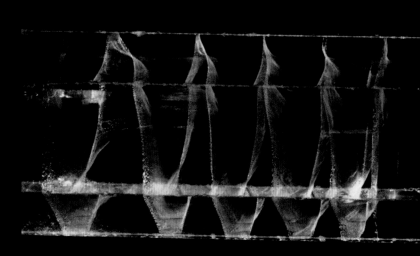

Emerald Variety of Beryl - Kagem Emerald Mine, Zambia, This very gemmy, 5 cm tall emerald on quartz is certainly one of the wonderful emerald specimens from this locality. It is amazing what the metal chromium does to color different mineral species. It is responsible, for the most part, for the green of emeralds, the reds of rubies and ruby spinels, the pink/oranges of "Imperial Topaz" from Brazil, the dark emerald green of Russian uvarovite garnets, and the bi-color effect of the highly sought after alexandrite variety of chrysoberyl. These color varieties are all caused by minute amounts of this metal. Chromium, and the metals: iron, cobalt, arsenic, manganese, vanadium, and titanium are major color contributors to Mother Nature's crystal palette.
Jeff Scovil photograph.

Emerald Variety of Beryl on Quartz, Kagem Mine, Zambia. (Lower Left) Emeralds on matrix are always a delight. The contrast of the intense green on cloudy white quartz focuses attention on the crystal. Specimen measures 3.8 cm tall. Jeff Scovil photograph.

Emerald Variety of Beryl on Quartz, Musquez Mine, Columbia. (Lower Right) This rare and pretty emerald specimen consists of four bright green and gemmy emerald crystals sitting on a color contrasting white quartz matrix. This emerald cluster stands 3.2 cm tall. Specimen measures 3.8 cm. Joe Budd photograph.

Topaz with Quartz "Halo", Shigar Valley, Pakistan. Only a few worldwide localities produced high-quality topaz specimens. Our favorite is this 8.9 cm wide by 7.5 cm high, cinnamon-colored gem crystal with a uniquely shaped terminated quartz crystal draped over the entire top. The quartz makes this topaz appear to have a quartz halo or hat. Joe Budd photograph.

Imperial Topaz, Ouro Preto, M.G., Brazil. (left) This beautiful single Imperial Topaz crystal features the highly sought after pinkish orange color which is prized in jewelry and collectable crystals. A less than 0.01% impurity of chromium oxide produces this luscious rich color. A common "tragically" for gem crystal collectors is that the best gem crystals are immediately cut for fine jewelry, because they are so valuable. The chase to find great specimens is sometimes exhausting, but it is also exhilarating to win the prized specimen. Through Keith and Mauna's travels in Brazil, they managed to "save" quite a few tourmaline, beryl, and topaz gem crystals from the cutters. Specimen measures 6.4 cm high. Jeff Scovil photograph,

Blue Topaz, Virgem da Lapa, M.G., Brazil. (right) This classic, well-terminated, blue Topaz crystal features distinctive sharp and wide top facets characteristic for this mine. This crystal is also highly textured on the right side, which adds to its beauty. Specimen measures 8.9 cm high and 8.9 cm wide. Joe Budd photograph.

Kunzite Variety of Spodumene, Nuristan, Afghanistan. (top left) This kunzite crystal measures 22.9 cm tall. The vertical sides are beautifully striated and the tip is uniquely shaped. This crystal is sitting on a nicely-sized matrix. The crystal is 3.2 cm wide and comes from an unknown mine in Nuristan, Afghanistan. Please compare this crystal's shape and termination with the one on the right, which is the typical Kunzite shape.
Joe Budd photograph.

Kunzite With Quartz, Nuristan, Afghanistan. (top right) The kunzite crystal on the top right has a white quartz crystal attached on the base. Specimen measures 15.2 cm tall.
Jeff Scovil photograph.

Kunzite, Resplendor Mine, M.G., Brazil. (lower left) This completely gem kunzite measures 15.2 cm tall and 6.4 cm wide, but it is only a maximum of 2.3 cm thick, which contributes to its spectacular and flashy appearance and its multitude of highly textured dissolution faces like the aquamarines described previously. This kunzite achieved its unique surface texturing from going back and forth, into and out of solution many times. Found near Resplendor city. Both sides of this extremely complex, luscious pink crystal invite our concentrated study with a bright light.
Joe Budd Photograph.

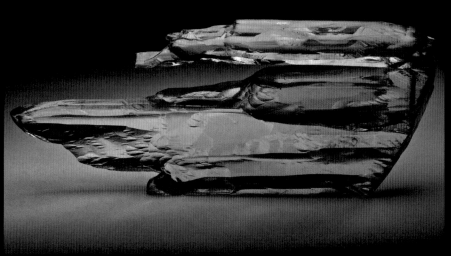

Tanzanite, Merelani Hills, Tanzania. (two views) Tanzanite is one of the scarcest and most sought after of all gem crystal species. It is coveted for its luscious blue and purple and sometimes red color flashes. To see all three of these colors in an uncut crystal is extremely rare indeed. When you face one side of this tanzanite crystal you see an intense blue, and by turning the crystal sideways you see a vibrant purple. But almost always, the only way you see the red color is if you look down the *b*-axis (the direction of crystal elongation). It is exciting to see a tanzanite gem crystal that, under normal photographic lighting, displays all three colors with the red flashing upward and diffusing throughout the crystal. The gemminess, the unusual "pyramid" shape, and the angle of some of the so-called veil inclusions in the base of this crystal allows it to scatter red light for maximum effect. If a tanzanite crystal shows a red color at any angle, this is strong evidence that it is a natural crystal, and it has not been heat-treated. This crystal was found in the Arusha valley, virtually in the shadow of Mount Kilimanjaro. Specimen measures 5.6 cm high. Jeff Scovil photograph.

Grossular Garnet on Green Diopside Crystals, Jeffrey Quarry, Asbestos, Québec, Canada. From near the city of Asbestos, Canada, we see a gemmy cinnamon-colored cluster of grossular garnets. Many of the finest and largest gem grossulars in the world came from the Jeffrey Quarry. This quarry also produced many best green and purple vesuvianite crystals. This specimen was dug in 1996 and measures 9.5 cm high, and displays gemmy crystals to 2.5 cm that are highly striated. The cinnamon color of these Jeffery quarry grossular crystals is caused by iron.
Joe Budd photograph.

Grossular Garnet, Jeffrey Quarry, Asbestos, Québec, Canada. This sherry-colored grossular specimen was acquired from the Dr. Ed David Collection in New Jersey. The specimen measures 7 cm across.
Jeff Scovil photograph.

Grossular Garnet with Diopside, Jeffrey Quarry, Asbestos, Québec, Canada. The Jeffrey Quarry produced a variety of superb garnet specimens and many would argue that the locality produced the world's largest and gemmiest grossular garnets. The open well-crystallized clusters seen here have crystals 1.9 cm to 2.5 cm across. These crystals also are striated, but with faces in a slightly different proportion than in garnet specimens #1 and 2. The triangular shaped specimen is well-covered with these isolated cinnamon colored grossular garnets on a diopside coated matrix This beautiful plate measures 13.3 cm wide, 10.2 cm high and 14.6 cm thick. Jeff Scovil photograph.

Grossular Garnet, Sierra de La Cruz, Mexico. (left and right) This specimen is a beautiful example from Sierra de la Cruz (Mountain of the Cross), which produced these delightful dark cranberry red garnets on matrix. This specimen, with its isolated crystals, is very attractive.

These grossulars are cranberry red because they have a high content of manganese, as an "impurity" not essential to the formula. Specimen measures 6.4 cm wide by 11.4 cm tall.

Joe Budd photographs.

Spessartine Garnet on Quartz, Tongbei, China. Shown here is a Smoky Quartz specimen with a 7.5 cm long crystal encrusted with gemmy, bright orange spessartine garnets. This is a restored specimen. This color results from the presence of manganese.
Joe Budd photograph.

Spessartine Garnet on Smoky Quartz, Microcline Feldspar, and Mica, Tongbei, China. This Smoky Quartz and crystallized microcline feldspar matrix is evenly sprinkled with bright, gemmy and more isolated spessartines than most Tongbei specimens. Even one "book" of mica is present. Specimen measures 7 cm wide by 8.9 cm high. It is uncommon to find all three present in good crystals on the same fine display specimen. Joe Budd Photograph.

Demantoid Garnets

Antetezambato, Ambanja Area, Antsiranana Region, Madagascar. One of the great locations of demantoid garnets is Madagascar; the other localities include the long extinct mine in the Malenco Valley, Italy and in Korkodin, Urals, Russia. The brilliant green color of these andradite Garnets is probably enhanced by minute amounts of chromium.
Joe Budd photographs.

Demantoid Garnets Antetezambato, Ambanja area, Antsiranana Region, Madagascar. Beautiful dodecahedral demantoid garnets with small trapezohedral faces. These specimens will surprise many people as garnets are stereotypically red. The depth of color and varied shades made this recent discovery an important one. Specimen measure: (top left) 6.4 x 5 cm, (top right) 19 x 10.2 cm, (lower left) 2.5 x 2.5 cm.

by Keith Proctor and Mauna Proctor   36

Quartz - The Most Common Mineral

Quartz is one of the most popular collector species, because of its wide range of colors and forms.
It is found associated with a wide variety of minerals as well as being found in beautiful crystals by itself.

Colorless Quartz with Hematite Rosettes, Jinlong, China. (left) Black hematite rosettes with four clear colorless quartz crystals. Specimen measures 8.3 cm wide and 7.5 cm high.
Joe Budd photograph.

Quartz and Red Hematite on Colorless Crystals, Jinlong mine China. (right) Quartz from this location in China may show only slight and irregular red to yellow hematite staining on some of its crystal surfaces, but the patches of color are vibrant because they are sitting on transparent crystals. Specimen measures 11.4 cm wide by 10.2 cm high.
Joe Budd photograph.

Red Quartz with Red Hematite Staining and with Black Hematite Rosettes, Jinlong Mine, Nanning Shan Area, China. (above) Three dozen bright quartzes show the red hematite trapped both inside and on the crystal surfaces. These red crystals are sitting on rosettes of black hematite. This specimen measures 8.9 cm wide and 14 cm long, Jeff Scovil photograph.

Quartz with Red Hematite Inclusions, Orange River, Namibia. (left) This is a bright red hematite-coated quartz specimen. The surface texturing of these red quartzes is also delightful. These quartzes are coated only on their surface layers and not impregnated throughout the matrix. Specimen measures 12.7 cm wide and 11.4 cm tall. From the Charlie Key collection.
Joe Budd photograph.

Quartz, Orange River, Namibia. (left) Each of the forty-plus quartz crystals grew in stages: first - white opaque quartz in the base; second, a red hematite coating on top of the first stage and finally a clear, gemmy pale pink termination due to a dusting of red hematite. This specimen measures 17.8 by 17.8 cm. These red inner included tips are called "phantoms".
Joe Budd photograph.

Quartz, Orange River, Namibia. (right) The opaque white quartz is capped with a brownish red hematite coating on the tips with phantoms inside. Then the brown thin layer is capped with a third growth of gemmy and slightly darker quartz. Specimen measures 15.2 cm wide and 12.7 cm tall. Joe Budd photograph.

Quartz, Second Sovietsky Mine, Dal'negorsk, Russia. This red quartz shows an unusual grouping of needle-like sprays of six sided crystals with sharp points. Specimen measures 10.2 cm wide and 14 cm tall. Joe Budd photograph.

by Keith Proctor and Mauna Proctor   40

Amethyst Quartz, Jacksons Crossroads, Wilkes County, Georgia, USA. This is a very nice amethyst specimen by any standard. It was on display at the Tucson, Arizona mineral show featuring "American Mineral Treasures". This beautiful specimen, measuring 12.7 cm wide by 16.5 cm high, is also pictured on page 254 of *American Mineral Treasures*. Joe Budd photograph.

Amethyst Variety of Quartz– Las Vigas Mine, Mexico. These delicate amethyst Quartz crystal tips are a luscious and vibrant purple and are evenly sprinkled over a 2.5 cm thick flat plate of small colorless quartzes. This appealing quartz plate measures 16.5 cm wide and 18.4 cm tall. The combination of both regular amethyst and also a few sceptered crystals creates a visually stunning specimen. Joe Budd photograph.

Color-Zoned Amethyst, Brandberg, Namibia. (above) Here we view a color-zoned amethyst quartz showing color phantoms that indicate internal variations in the mineral. Specimen measures 22.6 by 12.7 cm. Jeff Scovil photograph.

Amethyst Variety of Quartz. "The Rocket" - Guerrero Mine, Mexico. (above) Seen here is an exciting amethyst quartz crystal. Most Guerrero mine crystals display opaque purple bases and opaque white tips. This long, doubly terminated quartz crystal is perched at an angle looks like a rocket about to take off. The amethyst also has sharp color zoning on the tip of this gemmy crystal. Specimen measures 8.3 cm wide and 8.1 cm high. Joe Budd photograph.

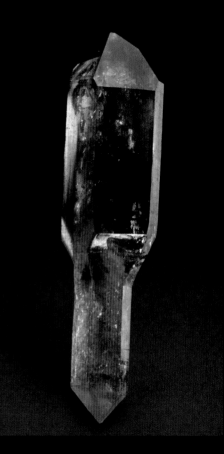

Amethyst Scepter, Brandberg, Goboboseb Mountains, Namibia. (right) The Brandberg area produced amethyst scepters some of that were doubly-terminated as is this one. This crystal is a so-called "floater specimen" with no point of attachment to a matrix. Specimen measures 8.9 cm long and 2.2 cm wide.
Joe Budd photograph.

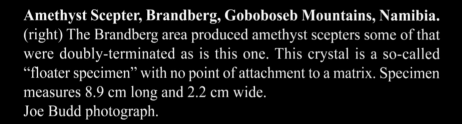

Amethyst Quartz, Artigas, Uruguay. (above) If this Amethyst knob were cut into thin slices, each slice would look like the amethyst slice at the lower left showing that these knobs grew in stages, producing concentric layers, the first of which was colorless quartz. Specimen measures 12.7 cm by 10.2 cm. Joe Budd photograph.

Amethyst "Dragon", Artigas, Uruguay. (above) This is an amethyst specimen shaped like a dragon's head. This "dragon" appears to be the friendly type, not the fire breathing variety. The Proctors have named this specimen "Puff the Magic Dragon" after a song about Hanalei Bay, Kauai, Hawaii that the Kingston Trio made famous in the 1960s. This fun "diversion" amethyst measures 7.5 cm wide and 12.7 cm tall. Joe Budd photograph.

Amethyst, Artigas, Uruguay. (lower left) Compare this Amethyst slice to the tall amethyst knob (upper left), The amethyst knob formed in concentric layers like an onion. We can see "growth rings" on this slice, which measures 10.2 cm wide and 9.5 cm high. Joe Budd photograph.

Amethyst Quartz, with Hematite-Stained Calcites. This masterpiece specimen comes from the Jonglushan mine, Hubei province, China. The presentation speaks for itself as each amethyst crystal is topped with a halo of red-stained Calcite crystals. Specimen measures 8.3 cm wide by 9.5 cm high. Jeff Scovil photograph.

Smoky Quartz Cluster - Uri, Switzerland. (above) Uri, Switzerland is the classic European locale for long, smoky quartz crystals on matrix. Specimen measures 15.2 cm wide by 14 cm deep. Jeff Scovil photograph.

Smoky Quartz, Mooralla, Victoria, Australia. (left) Small, but very fine, Australian smoky quartz cluster. Specimen measures 5 cm wide by 3.8 cm deep. Joe Budd photograph.

Quartz "Fish", Aracuai, Minas Gerais, Brazil. We view here possibly one of the greatest crystal specimens ever to escape its tomb in a granite pegmatite. We can marvel over this specimen time and again. It has received the name, "World's Greatest Stone Fish" and it is certainly the one that didn't get away. 40.6 cm-wide. The "fish" is complete with correct body shape, fins, tail, head, and scales; all displaying a multitude of golden brown smoky quartz crystal prisms and terminations. The Fish is unbroken and shows only crystallized quartz over the entire specimen's surface and has ideal proportions of length, width, and height. The only thing lacking for the complete effect was an eye; so we had one specially manufactured in Switzerland. The following three photos invite you to judge for yourself. Specimen measures 45.7 cm long by 22.9 cm high. Jeff Scovil photograph.

Quartz "Fish", Aracuai, Minas Gerais, Brazil. The minute quartz crystal terminations on the head and tail of this quartz "fish" look like scales. The head and face of the fish show what look are natural patterns and they are all crystallized quartz with no enhancement or man-made alterations of any kind. The "tail" is composed of slightly divergent quartz crystal terminations. An under sea background was inserted in order to return the fish to its home. Nathan King and Van King photographs.

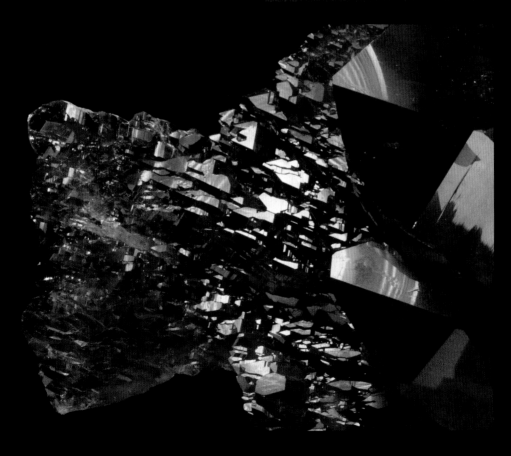

Quartz, McEarl Pocket, Mount Ida, Arkansas, USA. Undoubtedly millions of colorless quartz specimens have been found, but crystal connoisseurs agree that, because of their clarity and sculptural striations, the quartz crystals and crystal groups found several decades ago from the so-called McEarl pocket at the Coleman mine, Arkansas are "must haves". Specimen measures 20.3 cm high by 12.7 wide.
Jeff Scovil photograph.

Herkimer Diamond Variety of Quartz, Middleville, Herkimer County, New York, USA. Herkimer-style quartz crystals have been very popular since their discovery in the nineteenth century. Herkimer 'Diamonds" are frequently transparent, have a high luster, and have few or no surface markings. Because of their transparency, quartz crystals frequently are whimsically called "diamonds" and there are many places that have produced clear quartz crystals and have received this name. There are Cape May "Diamonds", Ellis River "Diamonds", etc. The Pecos River "Diamonds" abusively have that name as they are completely cloudy. Nonetheless, with their discovery, Herkimer Diamonds set the standard. This lovely suite of specimens was formerly in the Dr. Ed David collection. Top Left: 5 x 3.8 cm. Top Center: 4.4 x 2.5 cm. Top Right: 5 x 3.8 cm. Lower Left: 7.5 x 5 cm. Lower Center: 5 x 4 cm. Lower Right: 5x 3.8 cm. All photographs on this page by Joe Budd.

by Keith Proctor and Mauna Proctor   50

Quartz, Minas Gerais, Brazil. Here we see a so- called, animate or mimic specimen, which attracts interest. The quartz "whale" with both a perfect large dorsal fin and a pectoral fin seems to be in the process of eating black, shiny schorl tourmalines. A natural microcline feldspar crystal plate that is completely coated with small muscovite mica crystals is on the bottom side. Specimen measures 17.8 cm wide, 12.7 cm tall, and 5 cm thick. Joe Budd photograph.

Quartz with Pyrite, Spruce Claim, King County, Washington, USA. This is a nice combination piece. The quartz cluster is 17.8 cm wide and has a mirror-faced pyrite crystal perched on top. The pyrite has a dominant cubic shape with beveled corners showing the octahedron and long pointed diploid faces. Joe Budd photograph.

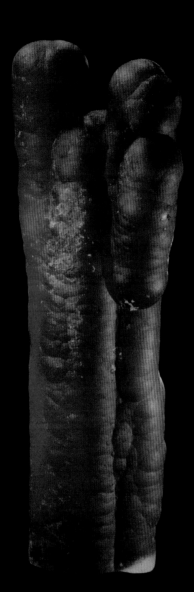

Chalcedony Variety of Quartz with Stilbite and Apophyllite, Nasik, India. (above left) Combination specimens are very popular from any location. This specimen shows clear apophyllite crystals with a pink stilbite on drusy quartz and chalcedony. Specimen measures 10.2 x 7.5 cm. Joe Budd photograph.

Red Chalcedony Quartz Spire, Java, Indonesia. (above center) Carnelian is a red variety of chalcedony and was formerly a precious stone. The columnar carnelian is translucent and the red color ranges throughout the specimen except for a small yellow patch of chalcedony at the base. Specimen measures 10.2 cm tall. Van King photograph.

Chalcedony Variety of Quartz Coating Calcite, Java Island, Indonesia. (above right) This chalcedony specimen is 24.1 cm long with surface bumps indicating the chalcedony was deposited over small calcite crystals. Lynn Sim photograph.

Dioptase, Tsumeb Mine, Namibia. Dioptase has a very unusual bluish green color and a typical specimen is shown here, but there are also small accents of yellow wulfenite crystals on the contrasting dolomite matrix. Dioptase and wulfenite were found together only at the famous Tsumeb Mine. 14.6 cm wide and 6.4 cm high. The detail of the center left of the specimen shown in the lower right view displays the terminations of the dioptase. Joe Budd photographs

Datolite, Dal'negorsk, Russia. (top right) This pale green datolite crystal is twinned and shows a central cleft dividing the two datolite crystals which are geometrically joined. It came from the Bor Pit (named for the boron minerals mined there). Specimen measures 10.2 cm high. There was an excellent article about these unusual twinned Datolite crystals in the *Mineralogical Record* magazine, (March –April 2009 issue, page 127). Joe Budd photograph.

Danburite, Charcas, San Luis Potosi, Mexico. The two "danburite" specimens in these two lower views really are quartz replacements of danburite (pseudomorphs). The word pseudomorph means "false form". These sparkly crystals exhibit the original form of the danburite crystals, but they are replaced by yellow quartz crystals. The danburite is completely gone and the quartz did not completely fill-in the interior. This specimen measures 15.2 cm tall and 7.5 cm wide. The first photo (lower right, Lynn Sim photograph) shows the top-side of this specimen with the yellow quartz pseudomorphs. The second photo (below left, Joe Budd photograph) shows the reverse side of this specimen with open cavities.

Danburite, Charcas Mine, San Luis Potosi, Mexico. The specimen pictured here is another quartz pseudomorph after danburite. It measures 30.5 cm wide, 25 cm deep, and stands 21.6 cm high. The quartz is tan colored and each pseudomorphed crystal is 7.5 cm wide. Joe Budd photograph.

Olmiite, N'chwanning II Mine, South Africa. (lower left) Lovely botryoidal cluster of tightly-intergrown orange olmiite. Manganese causes the beautiful color. Specimen measures 8.9 cm wide by 8.9 cm deep. Lynn Sim photograph.

Olmiite, N'chwanning II Mine, South Africa. (above right) This specimen shows a cluster of sharp olmiite crystals that have a pleasant pink color. The specimen view is 6.4 cm wide. Van King photograph.

Rhodonite, Chiurucu, Huánuco Department, Peru. (above) Red rhodonite blades in a radiating cluster. The rhodonite crystals are gemmy and show a slanting termination. Specimen measures 5 cm wide. Lynn Sim photograph.

Hemimorphite with Limonite, Ojuela Mine, Mapimi, Durango, Mexico. Hemimorphite almost always displays pure white to colorless sprays of bladed crystals. The matrix for this specimen is very instructive and shows 16 layers of the iron oxide limonite creating concentric shells. The open pocket measures 15.2 cm across. Hemimorphite formed within the last two layers. Specimen measures 20.3 cm high by 14 cm wide. Joe Budd photograph.

Hemimorphite with Adamite Crystals, Santa Eulalia, Chihuahua, Mexico. This hemimorphite specimen is a combination specimen with intermixed yellow adamite crystals. A nice touch is the pale red dusting of hematite on the hemimorphite tips. Specimen measures 10.2 cm wide x 11.4 cm tall.
Harold and Erica Van Pelt photograph.

Vesuvianite, Jeffrey Quarry, Asbestos, Québec, Canada. (above) The major crystal in this group has some prominent rare faces. There are two different sets of prisms called first-order prism and second order prism. They alternate around the crystal. The termination shows a steep ditetragonal pyramid and small second order bipyramid. This main crystal is 3.8 cm long, while the specimen measures 4.4 cm high and 2.5 wide. Jeff Scovil photograph.

Vesuvianite, Jeffrey Quarry, Asbestos, Québec, Canada. (above) This vesuvianite crystal cluster exhibits a different habit than the specimen on the left. It has a wide *c*-face creating a more rod-like appearance. The purple phantom core is characteristic of the Jeffrey Quarry vesuvianites. Specimen measures 3.8 cm high. Jeff Scovil photograph.

Chrysocolla and Malachite, Star of the Congo Mine, Lubumbashi, Katanga, Democratic Republic of Congo. (left) Chrysocolla is almost always a beautiful blue color and this one doesn't disappoint the collector. The crenulations of the botryoids provide an interesting flow of lines and the small dark green malachite crystals on the left are an added bonus. Specimen measures 7.5 cm wide x 10.2 cm tall. Lynn Sim photograph.

Amesite, Saranovskii Mine, Middle Urals, Russia. (above left) This specimen has purple columnar groups of purple, chromium-bearing pseudohexagonal amesite crystals. This specimen measures 6.4 cm tall and 4.4 cm wide. Joe Budd photograph.

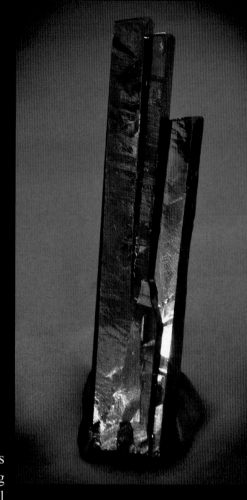

Aegirine, Mount Malosa, Zomba, Malawi. (above right) Seen here is a 8.9 cm high, 1.9 cm wide, vertical cluster of four almost parallel aegirine crystals displaying a jet-black patent-leather surface sheen. Lynn Sim photograph.

Ilvaite, Second Sovietsky Mine, Dal'negorsk, Russia. This is an aesthetic spray of ilvaite crystals. This specimen is from the Dr. Ed David collection. Specimen measures 6.4 cm wide and 7 cm high. Jeff Scovil photograph.

Cavansite on Stilbite Crystals, Wagholi Quarry Near Pune, India. (upper three specimens) This species exhibits stunningly beautiful blue crystals usually in spherical clusters. The white stilbite bed under the cavansite is the perfect background. Specimen measures 8.3 cm wide and 8.9 cm high. Joe Budd photographs.

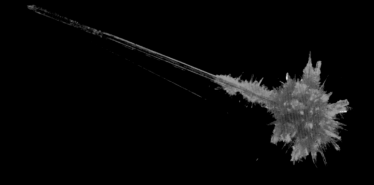

Pentagonite, Wagholi Quarry Near Pune, India. Pentagonite is a polymorph of cavansite meaning this species has the same formula, but a different crystal structure. This specimen is a kind of scepter with a cluster of spikes on a clear crystal rod. It measures 5 cm long.
Van King photograph.

by Keith Proctor and Mauna Proctor   60

Prehnite. Jebel Sermou, Khemisset region, Morocco. (top right) Distinct crystals of prehnite in clusters of delicately curved "flower petals". Prehnite is a species that almost always occurs as botryoidal masses in basalt with zeolites. Specimen measures 7 x 6.4 cm. Joe Budd photograph.

Prehnite on Epidote, Mount Malosa, Malawi. (above left) This is stack of sharp, shiny epidote crystals, hosting several green prehnite spheres. Specimen measures 17.8 x 8.9 cm. Sunnywood photograph.

Prehnite On Black Epidote Crystals, Malawi. Africa. (lower right) Here we see prehnite and greenish black epidote grown together. The prehnite forms textured and translucent green botryoids piled on top of an epidote matrix. 5.7 x 3.8 cm. Joe Budd photograph.

Cuprosklodowskite. Musonoi Mine, Katanga, Democratic Republic of Congo. Intense needle cuprosklodowskite crystals in a large vug. This specimen measures 10.2 x 7.5 cm. The stunning green color comes from a combination of its uranium and copper atoms, and this "electric" green color is virtually unique in the mineral kingdom. Lynn Sim photograph

Amazonite with Smoky Quartz, Tree Root Pocket, Pike's Peak Pegmatite Region, Colorado. (above left) Here we see a beautifully blue colored amazonite discovered by Bryan Lees. This cluster displays a smoky quartz crystal on the base. Acquired from the Dr. Steve Neely collection. This specimen was pictured in full color in *Rocks and Minerals* magazine. Specimen measures 11.4 cm wide by 7.5 cm high. Joe Budd photograph.

Microcline, Shengus, Baltistan, Pakistan. (above right) The pale pink microcline appears to be supported by two buttresses of black Tourmaline. The principal crystal is an uncommon Manebach twin. Specimen measures 12.7 x 8.9 cm. Lynn Sim photograph.

Phenakite, Momeik, Myan Mar. (lower left) This twinned Phenakite crystal nests on a perfect matrix of shiny feldspar with smoky quartz crystals. These twins are a cyclic arrangement of crystals. Specimen measures 5 cm wide; the largest crystal is 1.9 cm long. Van King photograph.

Muscovite Mica, Linópolis, Minas Gerais, Brazil. This is a beautiful, symmetrical and undamaged cluster of interlocked mica crystals, with each "crystal" being composed of multitudes of thin layered crystals. Specimen measures 17.8 cm wide and 16.5 cm high. Joe Budd photograph.

Muscovite, Linópolis, Minas Gerais, Brazil. Star mica is many people's favorite twin. The thin silvery yellow crystals form a six-rayed star. They are extremely fragile and the smallest touch can mar the look of the specimen. This piece shows a subtle horseshoe array of stars. Cluster measures 8.9 cm wide and 7.5 cm high. Joe Budd photograph

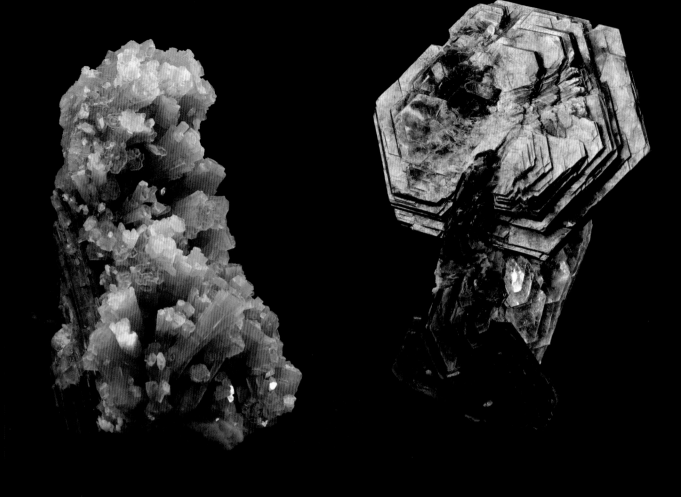

Lepidolite Mica, Pederneira Mine, M.G., Brazil. (top left) Well-formed rose-purple lepidolite crystals are frequently on collectors' acquisition lists. This 7.5 cm tall cluster of elongated and translucent lepidolite mica crystals is wonderful for the species. They seem to "flare" off from a green tourmaline crystal.
Joe Budd photograph.

Muscovite Mica, Zé Pinto Prospect, M.G., Brazil. (top right) Nice undamaged mica crystals, even if they are a common species such as muscovite, are not well-represented in collections. This aesthetic, 7.5 cm tall, hexagonal crystal of muscovite has a beautiful mauve shimmer in its interior.
Joe Budd photograph.

Muscovite, Shengus, Baltistan, Pakistan. (lower right) This is a twinned star mica crystal with a dark red brown garnet in the center. Specimen measures 14 cm wide by 12.7 cm high. Lynn Sim photograph.

Fluorite and Chemically Related Species The Halides.

Fluorite, Yaogangxian Mine, China. (above right) Gemmy ice-blue and purple fluorite. Note the interesting interpenetration lines of the various cubes. Specimen measures 6.4 x 6.4 cm. Jeff Scovil photograph.

Fluorite, Yaogangxing Mine, China. (left) This is a "Mayan pyramid-shaped" stack of cubic fluorite crystals with small beveling faces. This unusual group is dusted by micro brassy pyrite crystals. 7.5 wide and 4.4 cm. Joe Budd photograph.

Fluorite, Yaogangxian Mine, China. (lower right) Except for the unusual large cube on the points, this fluorite is a very complete Mayan pyramid. 8.9 x 8.3 cm. Jeff Scovil photograph.

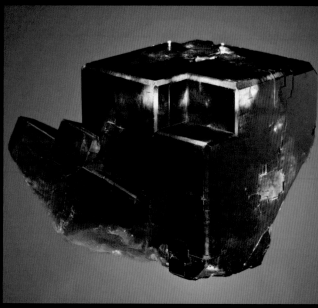

Fluorite, Berbes Mine, Asturias, Spain. (upper right) The Berbes mining area produced multitudes of specimens with small pale purple or yellow cubes sometimes on white bladed barite, but this crystal has a very intense purple color. Specimen measures 8.6 cm wide by 5 cm tall. Jeff Scovil photograph.

Fluorite, Annabell Lee Mine, Cave-In-Rock, Hardin County, Illinois, USA. (upper left) Pinkish purple fluorite is a very special color, especially when the fluorite is composed of seemingly randomly interpenetrating cubes. This specimen measures 10.2 x 10.2 x 6.4 cm. Joe Budd photograph.

Fluorite, Nikolai Mine, Dal'negorsk, Far Eastern Region, Russia. (lower left) We see here a very "sculptural", 7.5 cm green cube of gemmy fluorite perched on the very top edge of the matrix. A few internal cleavage planes are an advantage to the viewer because they cause the light to refract and disperse beautifully. Specimen measures 12.7 cm wide, 15.2 cm tall and only 3.8 cm thick. Joe Budd photograph.

Fluorite, Yaogangxian Mine, China. Multi-colored fluorite is always a delight and when it displays several stacks of cube fluorites, the joy is complete. The largest cube, 3.8 cm across, presents dark purple corners creating an elegant display piece. 7.5 x 7.5 x 7.5 cm. Joe Budd photograph.

Fluorite, Yaogangxian Mine, China. Here ten fluorite crystals with dark purple centers grew on a clear quartz crystal cluster. 12.7 x 10.2 cm. Joe Budd photograph.

Fluorite, Yaogangxian Mine, China. Mint green cubes with purple centers. 6.4 x 7 cm. Jeff Scovil photograph.

Fluorite, Elmwood Mine, Carthage, Smith County, Tennessee, USA. (upper right) On this specimen, we see more than 20 gemmy purple fluorite cubes dispersed in an isolated fashion. The white matrix makes for a perfect color contrast allowing the crystals to stand out. Specimen measures 20.3 cm wide x 15.2 cm tall x 8.9 thick. Jeff Scovil photograph.

Fluorite, Xianghualing Mine, China. (below left) These amazing crystals are so clear one could read a newspaper through them. We can even clearly see the texture of the green matrix underneath. Specimen measures 11.4 cm wide by 7 cm high. Joe Budd photograph.

Fluorite, Okorusu, Otjozondjupa Region, Namibia. (upper left) Color zoning rarely gets as pretty as this. Colorless zones on cranberry-red is striking, but these fluorite crystals also quickly grade to reddish black in their centers producing a dramatic effect. Specimen measures 11.4 cm wide by 10.2 tall.
Lynn Sim photograph.

Fluorite, Múzquiz, Coahuila, Mexico. (lower left) This is a 9.5 cm stack of small purple fluorite cubes running up the center of a celestine crystal.16.5 cm high by 8.9 cm wide and only 0.95 cm thick. Because of color contrast, form, and composition it is an interesting specimen. Joe Budd photograph.

Fluorite, Minerva #1 Mine, Cave-In-Rock, Hardin County, Illinois, USA. (lower right) Displayed here is a beautiful specimen of superb rich yellow fluorite cubes ranging up to 5 cm across. Small chalcopyrite crystals are seen dotting the surface of the cubes. Specimen measures 14 cm wide, 12.7 cm tall and 6.4 cm thick. Acquired from the famous Jim Minette collection. Joe Budd photograph.

Fluorite, Riemvasmaak, Cape Province, South Africa. (left) This is an outstanding green octahedral fluorite specimen that measures 8.9 cm wide by 10.2 cm tall. Jeff Scovil photograph.

Fluorite, Goshenen Alp, Switzerland. (right) This magnificent 5 cm cluster of rose-colored, sharp octahedrons of fluorite come from the most classic location: Switzerland near the St. Gotthard tunnel before going into Italy, It was dug by one of the intrepid Swiss strahlers (alpine diggers) decades ago. Of all classic fluorites, pink Swiss octahedral fluorite crystals are among the most coveted and sought after by connoisseur collectors. Acquired from the Dr. Neely collection. Specimen measures 8.3 cm high, and 7.5 cm wide. Jeff Scovil photograph.

Fluorite, Xianghualing Mine, Hunan Province, China. (above) Fluorite is a beautiful mineral and sometimes it occurs in two generations of growth resulting in bi-colored crystals. These crystals are blue octahedral crystals on the outside that were overlain on green fluorite. The octahedral fluorite crystals are 5-7 cm. 17. 12.7 cm x12.7 cm x 10.2 cm. Joe Budd photograph.

Fluorite, Xianghualing Mine, China. (left) Two colors of fluorite on a specimen but in different crystals is remarkable. These crystals are not bi-colored. There is a large green, ideal octahedron on top with smaller purple octahedrons underneath that formed during a different growth phase. This makes a spectacular presentation. 15.2 x 10.2 cm.

Joe Budd photograph.

Fluorite, Riemvasmaak, Cape Province, South Africa. (upper right) Many collectors specialize in just one or a few mineral species. This specimen is a great example of why there are such specialized collectors. The crystals have an amazing vibrant green color, the crystals have a pleasing shape, and they are gemmy. 4.4 x 6.4 cm. Joe Budd photograph.

Fluorite, Jalgaon, Maharashtra, India. (left) Spherical mineral shapes are called botryoids and they are the pearls of the mineral kingdom. These unusual yellow fluorite botryoids on quartz are translucent and have cat's-eye chatoyancy when under bright lights. Specimen measures 12 x 13.3 cm. Jeff Scovil photograph.

Fluorite, De'an Mine, Jiangxi, China. (lower right) Individual fluorite crystals on matrix can be very showy. This octahedron proudly displays its pyramidal appearance and has purple accents on the edges and points with a window revealing the green interior. The crystal rests on a creamy white quartz matrix. 8.3 x 7 x 3.8 cm. Joe Budd photograph.

Fluorite, Nagar, Pakistan. (above right) Pastel bi-color fluorite crystals have a distinct beauty, especially when transparent. This light pink and delicate lime green octahedral fluorite crystal rests on bladed muscovite mica. 7.5 x 10.2 x 7.5 cm. Acquired from the Dr. Ed David collection. Joe Budd photograph.

Fluorite, Jiangxi, China. (upper left) One of the very interesting features on crystals may be their evidence of reaction to the fluids that formed them. This fluorite is a combination of the cube and the octahedron in nearly equal proportions. The square faces are related to the cube shape and each one has a rough, etched surface, while the adjacent triangular faces, related to the octahedron, are smooth and undisturbed. The quartz crystals are 1-2.5 cm. 9.5 x 10.2 cm. Joe Budd photograph.

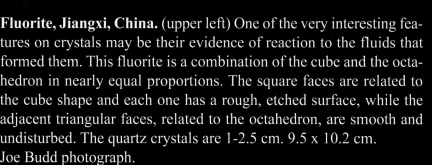

Fluorite, De'an Mine, Jiangxi, China. (lower left) Here we see an absolutely perfect, exceedingly dark purple, single, fourteen sided, cubo-octahedron sitting on top of a white thin quartz "cone". The De'an Mine is noted for producing the best examples of these rare, purple, cubo-octahedrons. Note the hexagonal crystal on the top left as well, this hexagonal face is one of the diagnostic "finger prints" to identify a classic cubo-octahdral crystal. Specimen measures 10.2 x 10.2 and 7.5 cm high. Joe Budd photograph

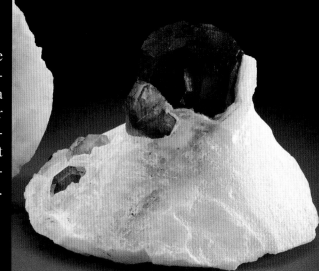

Fluorite, De'an Mine, China. (above) Purple fluorite frequently shows only cube faces and it is a treat to see several forms present on this specimen. When the cube and octahedron faces are in about equal proportions, the triangle you'd expect on an octahedron face is partially cut by the cube face so the octahedral face can look like a hexagon. 7.5 cm tall. Joe Budd photograph.

Thenardite, After Halite, Searles Lake, San Bernardino County, California, USA. (lower left) These hoppered (concave) crystals of halite have been replaced by thenardite and are a pseudomorph. The thenardite crystals replaced the shape of the halite crystals. Specimen which measures 10.2 cm high and 7.5 cm wide. Joe Budd photograph.

Halite, Searles Lake, California, USA. A hoppered crystal is concave, with the outside edges being much higher than the center of the face (the hopper). The pink color halite is caused internally by harmless halo-bacteria that originally lived in the brine that formed the salt. Specimen measures 17.1 cm wide by 10.2 cm deep. Van King photograph.

Native Elements
Gold, Silver, Copper, Sulphur, Bismuth, Carbon, Mercury

Gold – The Noble Metal

What is the mystique surrounding gold? Gold is that one mineral that excites virtually everyone. No other mineral has had a greater power over human greed than gold. Many frontiers were explored and settled - including the Western U.S., Western Australia, and Western Brazil by gold prospectors. Considering the Mayan, Aztec and Incan civilizations, entire nations and cultures were destroyed in the wake of gold's pursuit. Many wars were financed by both gold and, its noble cousin, silver. Kingdoms were won and lost because of their allure. Chemists called gold the noble metal because its stubborn atoms seldom form complex mineral compounds.

Throughout history, gold has excited a fever pitch in mankind. This passion was never more obvious than in the fairy tales ("Midas Touch" and "Rumpelstiltskin") or in the stories of sunken Spanish galleons and their treasures. Much of Florida's east coastline is named "The Gold Coast" because of the treasure from the galleons that continues to appear there. Hundreds of millions of dollars in gold and silver bullion, chains, and coins have been salvaged from this area alone. These shipwreck and salvage stories fire people's imaginations as they fantasize themselves possibly finding a "pirate's treasure".

The most famous salvage recovery is the Atocha that sunk in a hurricane in 1622 off the Florida Keys and was recovered near Key West. The second most famous story is legendary as well. It is the salvage of the 11 Spanish gold and silver laden galleons that were sunk off the east coast of Florida in the great hurricane of 1715. These wrecks were strewn up and down the Florida coast between the current Cape Canaveral (Cocoa Beach) on the north and Vero Beach on the south with the Sebastian inlet in between. This small inlet was an opening from the Indian "River" inter-coastal waterway out into the Atlantic Ocean. (The U. S. Navy bombed this inlet partially shut because German submarines actually entered the Indian "River" during World War II.) As a teenager Mr. Proctor lived three miles from Sebastian Inlet. He went sea fishing with his father off the north side of the inlet, and they constantly fouled their lines on something 200 feet offshore. With one hurricane, gold coins washed up on the beach, and several years later a National Geographic story chronicled the salvage of one of the eleven ships from the 1715 disaster near the mouth of the Sebastian Inlet. Keith is certain this was the wreck that stole so much of their fishing tackle. These wrecks produced many gold coins and one of them is shown in a jewelry mount, both front and back (4.1 x 3.8 cm). Van King photographs.

by Keith Proctor and Mauna Proctor

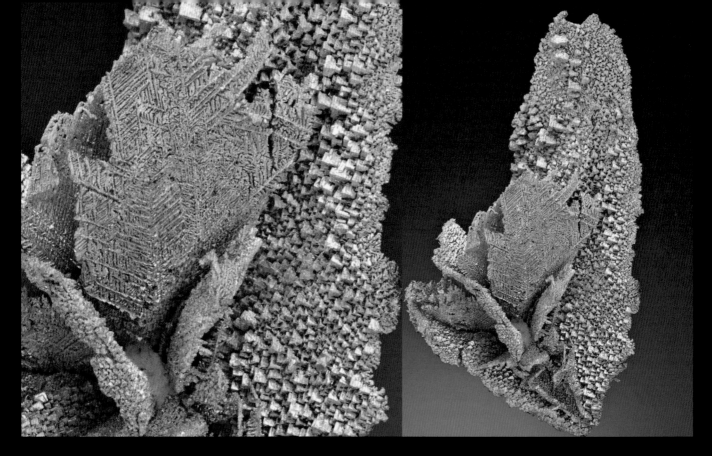

Gold, Round Mountain Mine, Nevada, USA. Cubic gold is one of the most sought after of gold crystal shapes, but their popularity is closely rivaled by the spinel-law-twinned, herringbone habit. This specimen features both types (see detail on the upper left). Herringbone crystal growth pattern, as the name implies, has a central spine with mirror-image branches coming off both sides of their spinel-twin along the length of the spine. Specimen measures 6.4 cm high. Jeff Scovil photograph.

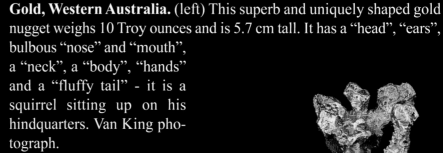

Gold, Western Australia. (left) This superb and uniquely shaped gold nugget weighs 10 Troy ounces and is 5.7 cm tall. It has a "head", "ears", bulbous "nose" and "mouth", a "neck", a "body", "hands" and a "fluffy tail" - it is a squirrel sitting up on his hindquarters. Van King photograph.

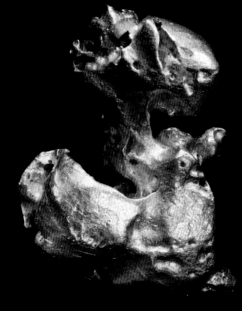

Gold, Berezovskoe Mine, Middle Urals, Russia. (right) Sometimes aesthetics speak louder than analysis. This is a 4.4 cm tall by 3.2 cm wide crystallized nugget. It was published in the English version of the extraLapis book. *Gold,* on page 7. Lynn Sim photograph.

Gold, Round Mountain Mine, Nye County, Nevada, USA. Great gold specimens are more precious every year, but in the last few decades, newly discovered specimens seem to have better crystals. This 10.2 cm wide specimen has a leaf as its platform for skeletal octahedral gold crystals. They grew all the way around the top of this specimen as well as on the sides. This gold is somewhat silver-rich giving a slightly paler yellow color than silver-poor gold. The quartz matrix offers a nice compliment. Joe Budd photograph.

Gold, Round Mountain Mine, Nevada, USA Luscious leaves made of curved, interwoven, herringbone, spinel-twinned crystals and flat, elongated, bar-shaped spinel-twins. Specimen measures 5.5 cm wide by 4.3 cm high.
Richard Jackson photograph.

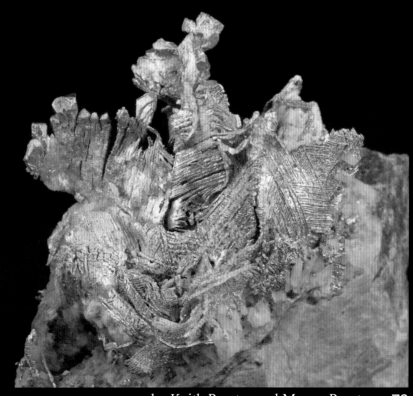

Gold, Round Mountain Mine, Nevada, USA.
(right) Texture is an important quality in mineral specimens. Gold from Round Mountain is beautiful and complex. This thin gold crystal cluster displays brilliant shiny crystals that have a tightly interwoven herringbone pattern. Twinning of multitudes of cube-shaped gold crystals is so tightly "woven" that it looks like cloth fabric. Specimen measures 7.5 cm tall by 13.8 cm wide. Jeff Scovil photograph.

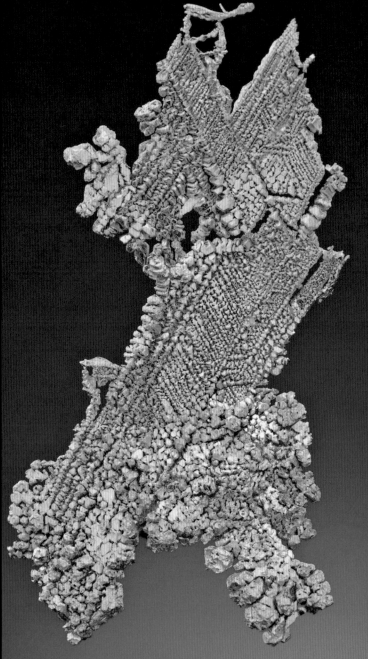

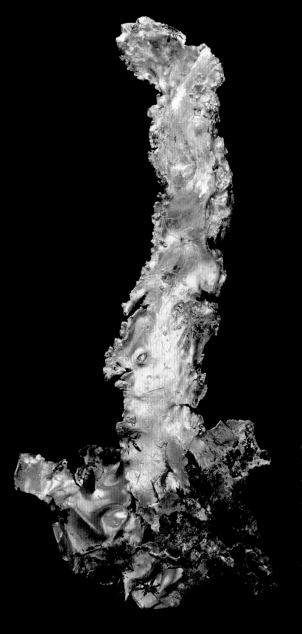

Gold Leaf, Red Ledge Mine, Nevada County, California USA. (left) This mine produced some of the world's best and biggest leaf golds, and they are virtually never seen on the market. The Proctors acquired this masterpiece specimen from the famous Mark Weill collection after it was featured in the Mark Weill Collection supplement published by *Mineralogical Record* magazine, January-February 2008. 22.9 cm tall. Jeff Scovil photograph.

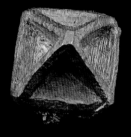  

Gold, Siberia, Russia. (three views) Ideally, octahedral crystals have eight flat triangular faces. Hoppered crystals such as these are caused by rapid so-called "skeletal growth". The edges had gold added faster than the center triangular faces did. While this habit is not uncommon, especially in very small crystals, this one is astonishing for its size and sharpness. The crystal measures approximately 2.5 cm. The crystal seen in these three views is "complete", showing all eight faces, not to mention the complete hoppered aspect on each face. Lynn Sim photographs.

Gold, Round Mountain Mine, Nevada, USA. (right and below) These are two views of a delightful feathery gold specimen (front side and reverse side). This well-crystallized gold crystal cluster measures 5 cm wide. The "front side" of the specimen on the right is made up of many fern-like clusters or "fronds" of spinel-law-twinned crystals in a herringbone pattern. There are some twinned cubes along the center spines. This is an inviting specimen for the imagination.
Jeff Scovil photograph.

(left) The "reverse side" of the gold specimen displays a similar crystallization, but with some stronger appearing fronds. Most of the fronds are made up of a tightly interwoven herringbone pattern and their spinel-twin center spines display a few cubes. Jeff Scovil photograph.

Gold, Round Mountain Mine, Nevada, USA. (above) This is a leaf gold studded with crystallized gold al around the edges, with both flat and raised octahedrons, some with cubo-octahedral habit. The top left side o he leaf displays an "Eagle's head". Because this gold has a high silver content, it has a lighter color than gold rom many other localities. This stunning specimen measures 10.2 cm wide. Lynn Sim photograph.

Gold Leaf, Shore Mine, Tuolumne County, California, USA. (right) Gold leaf specimens are always in great demand. This specimen presents a highly textured raised rim of crystals around the edges of this leaf. Specimen measures 8.3 cm wide. Lynn Sim photograph.

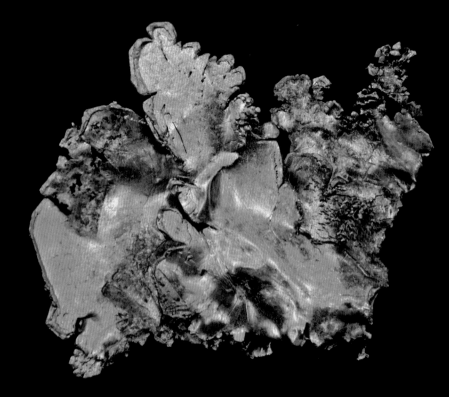

Gold, Round Mountain Mine, Nevada, USA. (left) Mineral collectors love to have as many specimens of gold on quartz as they can. This 7.5 x 7.5 cm specimen displays a large, flat array of spinel-twinned gold crystals. The center structure measures 3.2 cm on an edge and this image was previously published in *Mineralogical Record*, March/April 2009, page 104.
Joe Budd photograph.

The detail image (right) focuses on the rows of gold crystals, arranged in side-by-side vertical rows mimicking a beaded curtain. These rows of "beads" are made up entirely of stacked cubes on a center spine of minute spinel-twins. On the upper left edge there is a concentration of cubo-octahedral crystals. The quartz crystals are terminated as well.
Joe Budd photograph.

Acanthite, Imiter Mine, Morocco. (right) The acanthite crystals from the Imiter mine were frequently large, but crude with dull surfaces. The bright and shiny crystals on this specimen are extremely sharp, allowing one easily study the pyramidal shape of these isolated crystals. Specimen measures 7.5 cm high.
Jeff Scovil photograph.

Acanthite, Hongda mine, Shanxi Province, China. Seen are front and back views of stacks of acanthite cubes. This specimen measures 7.5 by 5 cm and the largest chunky cube measures 3.2 cm long. Many silver wires, worldwide, are said to be produced during the dissolution of acanthite crystals.
Lynn Sim photographs.

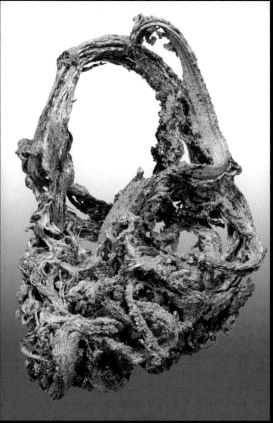

Silver Wires - Imiter Mine Morocco. (upper left and below right) Silver wires always seem to please our aesthetic nature and when the wires are curled as though they were ropes, the specimen is at its best. We rate this 5.7 cm high silver specimen as superb. Joe Budd photograph.

Proustite, Dolores Mine, Chañarcillo, Chili. (lower left) This silver and arsenic species was named after the French chemist Joseph Louis Proust (1754-1826), and the iconic mine that produced the world's best proustite is the Dolores mine, but it has been closed for many decades. Proustite crystals contain silver and can be a brilliant red, although they are light sensitive and darken when exposed to light for a long time. This 7.5 cm tall specimen of gemmy red crystals is compelling. Joe Budd photograph.

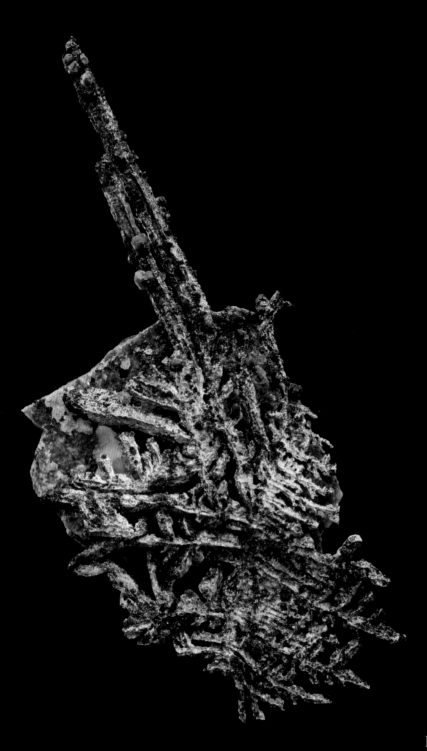

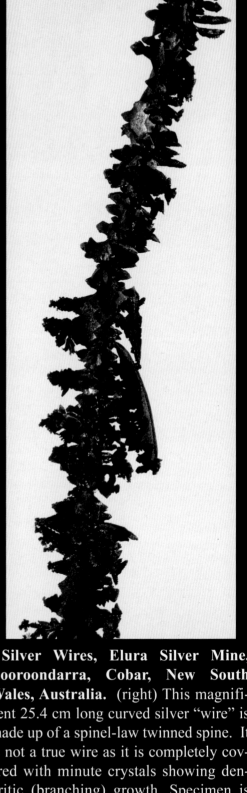

Silver Wires, Elura Silver Mine, Booroondarra, Cobar, New South Wales, Australia. (right) This magnificent 25.4 cm long curved silver "wire" is made up of a spinel-law twinned spine. It is not a true wire as it is completely covered with minute crystals showing dendritic (branching) growth. Specimen is from the famous Jim Minette collection. Specimen measures 17.8 cm long. Joe Budd photograph.

Silver, Botapilas, Chihuahua, Mexico. (left) The specimen displays all herringbone-growth silver crystals on a small quartz matrix. This specimen measures 7 cm high and 3.2 cm wide. There are a few small spheres of black acanthite on the two main vertical spinel twin spines. The Proctors have gone 5000 feet deep down into the Copper Canyon to see the Botapilas mine. It was once visited by Pancho Villa who threatened the American mine manager and gave him one day to "get out". Joe Budd photograph.

Silver Wires, Freiberg, Germany. (upper right)
This is a spectacular, old-time wire silver. Specimen measures 16.5 cm high by 8.9 cm wide.
Note how wide the wires are at their base. The
base of the largest wire is 2.5 cm across.
Joe Budd photograph.

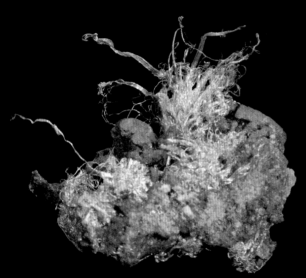

Silver Wires on Acanthite, Imiter Mine, Morocco. (left) Seen here is an acanthite crystal in
the center between two sprays of silver wire
sprouting near it. Specimen measures 4.2 x 4 cm.
Van King photograph.

Wire Silver and Acanthite, Imiter Mine, Morocco. (lower right) Wire silver sprouting off the
top of black acanthite. Specimen measures 4.2 cm
wide by 4 cm high. Van King photograph.

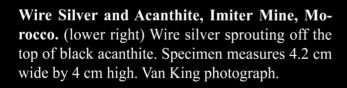

Wire Silver, The Kings Mine, Kongsberg, Norway. Kongsberg produced the world's finest wire silver specimens and, rarely, produced silver crystals. We love the aesthetics of this specimen, because it features a crude, but distinct 4.4 cm cubo-octahedral silver crystal. This crystal rests on curved branches of silver. For compactness and sheer artistry, this is another of the Proctors' favorite specimens. There is an interesting story with this specimen. The Kings Mine was started in 1624 and was "officially" closed in 1957. Even 300 years ago miners certainly high graded (stole) valuable specimens. Some miner hid this specimen under a rock in one of the side tunnels, intending to come back quietly and retrieve it when his supervisors were not watching. The day never came when the miner retrieved this prize. In 2006, an intrepid climber, using ropes, descended deep inside this dangerous, cavernous mine, hoping to fulfill his fantasy of finding a fine wire silver. He found nothing initially but he went for a moment into a small alcove. While there, he turned over a rock and hidden underneath it was this masterpiece. Specimen measures 7.5 cm wide by 10.2 cm high. Jeff Scovil photograph.

Wire Silver, Ducat, Far-Eastern Region, Russia. (right) Wire silver is a very popular mineral, but good specimens are uncommon. This specimen was named: "The Cobra". Specimen measures 8.3 cm high, but the silver wire is 15.2 cm long! Jeff Scovil photograph.

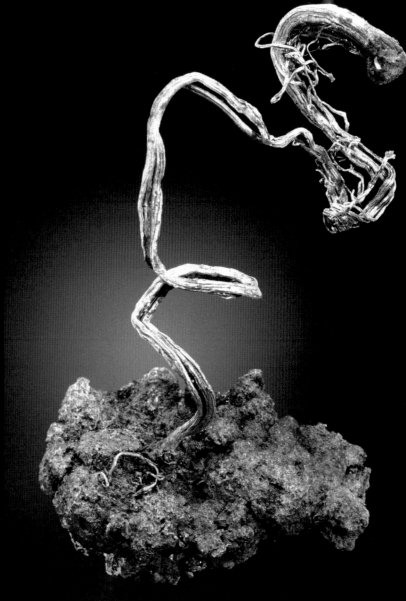

Silver and Copper, Keweenaw Peninsula, Michigan, USA. (left" This miniature-sized masterpiece displays both crystallized silver and copper together. The specimen measures 5 cm wide by 3.8 cm high, but flaring vertically out of the copper crystal, is a 2.5 cm tall stack of five distorted silver crystals. This beautiful silver structure sits on a foil-like 2.5 cm long spinel-twin copper crystal. In the center of the specimen is a small, rounded dodecahedral copper crystal. Joe Budd photograph.

The Keith and Mauna Proctor Family Trust Collection

Silver, Keweenaw Peninsula, Michigan, USA. (front and back views) This delightful twinned Michigan silver crystal cluster sits on a matrix of silver and copper. Historically, these have been called "half-breed" specimens because the two metals do not mix with each other, but remain separate. Half-Breed specimens seldom display large silver crystals as this one does. In this silver, we sometimes see a squirrel on its back or perhaps a sea creature with fins outstretched appendages "reaching" upwards. Specimen measures 3.8 cm high.
Joe Budd photographs

Copper, Keweenaw Peninsula, Michigan, USA. "The Praying Mantis" form is obvious in this huge specimen. The entire surface of this copper specimen sports crystals that are 5 to 6.4 cm. Many of the crystals are elongated crystals. Keith traded this wonderful specimen with Dr. Ed David. Specimen measures 22.9 cm long by 12.7 cm high and has no point of contact, so this is a so-called, floater specimen.
Joe Budd photograph.

Copper, Keweenaw Peninsula, Michigan, USA. Big chunky crystals of copper with interesting and rare shapes are exceedingly sought after by collectors and this specimen would be welcome everywhere. Note the well defined separate crystals. Specimen measures 8.3 by 6.4 cm.
Lynn Sim photograph.

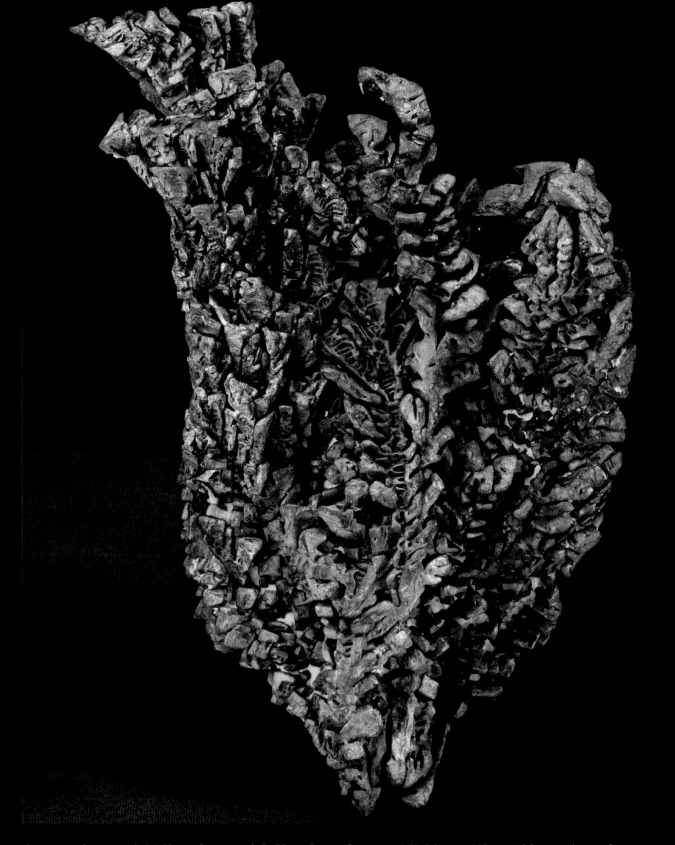

Copper, Centennial Mine, Centennial, Houghton County, Michigan, USA. This specimen features cubic copper crystals with spinel-twin herringbone texture. The specimen has many branches, each with a slightly different appearance. The spinel-twin spines acted as a template for the formation of these stacked cubes, just as was shown in the gold specimens from the Round Mountain Mine, Nevada. Specimen measures 10.2 cm high by 7 cm wide. Joe Budd photograph.

Copper, Keweenaw Peninsula, Michigan, USA. (above) This wonderful, highly textured cluster of twinned copper crystals flares off the top of a copper matrix. Note the twinning lines on the crystal. Specimen measures 3.8 by 3.8 cm. Joe Budd photograph.

Copper, Centennial Mine Keweenaw, Peninsula, Michigan, USA. (two views right) Good cubes of copper are rare, and this specimen sports a well-defined hoppered cube in addition to other cubes on thick copper wires. Specimen measures 11.4 cm high by 5 cm wide. Van King photographs.

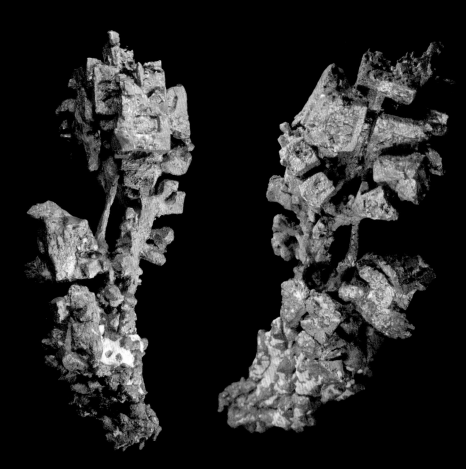

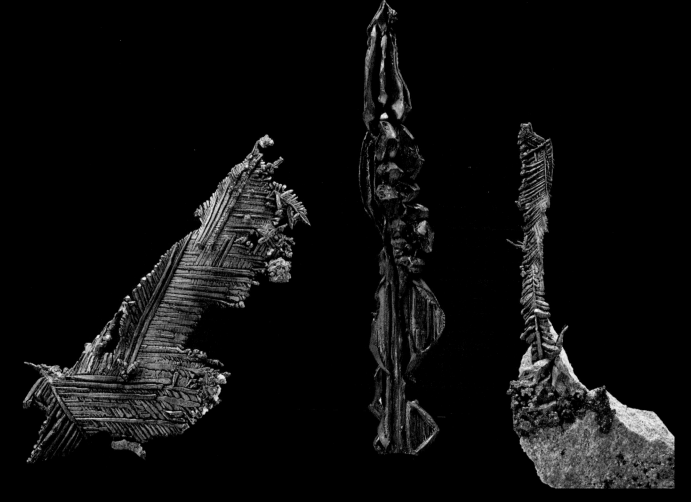

Copper, Dzhezkazgan, Karagandy Province, Kazakhstan. These are three very interesting herringbone-textured copper specimens composed of spinel-law-twinned crystals. In the right and left specimens, the obvious spinel-law-twin center spine has side spire branches. In comparing the appearance of these three copper specimens with the specimen on the previous pages, we can see how spinel-law-twin spines act as a template for the formation of the cubic copper crystals and similarly with the gold specimens from the Round Mountain Mine in Nevada. Above specimens measure 7 to 7.5 cm tall, and each tells it own story. Joe Budd photograph.

Franklin Mine, Houghton County, Michigan, USA. (upper right) These doubly terminated, parallel-growth calcite scalenohedron-shaped crystals act as a cocoon for native copper crystals trapped inside. The delicate striations on these calcite crystals are wonderful. Specimen measures 6.4 by 3.8 cm.
Van King photograph.

Copper After Azurite, Georgetown, Grant County, New Mexico, USA. (lower left) This is a double pseudomorph: copper after malachite after azurite. Originally it was malachite after azurite. It is difficult to visualize how the rosette-shaped azurite crystals' surface could have altered to malachite and then to copper. Specimen measures 3.8 cm high. Joe Budd photograph.

Copper After Aragonite, Corocoro, La Paz Department, Bolivia. (lower right) This is a fine example of a sharp pseudomorph of copper after the aragonite. Specimen measures 3.8 cm high.
Joe Budd photograph.

by Keith Proctor and Mauna Proctor

Graphite, Gouverneur Talc #4 Pit, Diana, Lewis County, New York, USA. (upper left) Graphite may form large masses of foliated mineral weighing tons, but crystals are very uncommon. These are rosettes of brilliant black platy hexagonal graphite crystals in blue calcite. 8 x 10 cm.
Van King photograph.

Graphite, Johnsburg, Warren County, New York, USA. (lower right) Foliated gray graphite crystals in goethite-stained quartz matrix. 9 x 9 cm.
Van King photograph.

Sulphur, Agrigento, Sicily, Italy. Here we see a superb example of a sulphur crystal, which is very gemmy on a matrix of celestine. One of the best qualities the crystal has is its reasonably balanced crystal faces. Specimen measures 7 cm wide. Van King photograph.

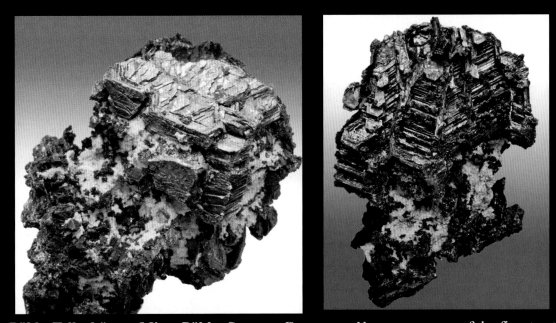

Bismuth, Pöhla-Tellerhäuser Mine, Pöhla, Saxony, Germany. Here we see one of the finest native bismuth specimens ever offered for sale in the United States. Specimen is 7 cm high, and features extremely rare and sharp, striated bismuth crystals on matrix. Lynn Sim photograph.

Chapter Two: *The Legacy Continues*
by Brice Gobin and Christophe Gobin

In 1974, Christian Gobin, our late father, a lifelong mineral collector, formed GOBIN MINERAUX, a mineral dealership. It was his passion for mineralogy that led him to his business model of traveling extensively in search of fine mineral specimens to sell to his discriminating clients. He did this with zeal and success until 1996. We followed in his path. We travel far and wide throughout the year to collect the finest of gems and minerals in order to bring them to our clients. Our passion has become a way of life.

Our "hunting fields" are usually in Africa and Asia, especially from the Democratic Republic of Congo, Tanzania, Namibia, Pakistan, Afghanistan, China, Morocco and anywhere else it "smells" good for new mineral finds!

Brice Gobin
and Christophe Gobin

The pursuit of the ultimate piece is always our chase. Quality is the center of our hunt. Beauty, color, rarity, we live by this triad; it is our basis, and indeed our philosophy, for selecting the finest minerals. It is not complicated, but it is challenging to accomplish. Paulo Coehlo, the famous author of "The Alchemist" wrote: "When we have great treasures right under our eyes, we never see them. And do you know why? Because men do not believe in treasure." Minerals are real. They do exist and there are wondrous crystal treasures from the Earth. We regard crystals as our planet's legacy. They are the "Prime Art". We believe that minerals deserve our attentive quest and that is why we do not give up. Of course, there are times when going to the source provides nothing except a reason to go home, but we are committed and we are driven by the possibilities of the next time. Going to the source is our elixir. It is a way to immerse ourselves into the lives of the people at the place of discovery. We do all we can to merge with the people; we dress like the locals (sometimes for security reasons), we eat from the same plates, we sleep in local villages in the middle of nowhere and we love it, all of it!

When we return to our world, we have stories to share with our family, friends, customers and all the other fellows in this hobby. When we are fortunate, we also have minerals! Every mineral specimen that we provide has a story to tell; that's our signature. From the foothills of Mount Kilimanjaro in Tanzania, to the hills of Chumar Bakhoor in the Hunza valley in Pakistan, we will continue to do our ultimate to bring to light outstanding mineral specimens.

Thanks, Dad, for sharing your passion of mineralogy with us.
Your legacy lives on.

The Himalayas are not only beautiful, they are producers of fine gem crystals and they are also a hazard to airplane navigation. The scenery is gorgeous, but there are tiny airports which can only be reached through dangerous passes. Photograph courtesy of Jim Clanin.

While it is true that "gold is where you find it", gem crystals are frequently found in inconvenient locations. This is a steep mountainside near Gilgit in Northern Pakistan. The gem-bearing pegmatites are in the thin white veins and dark holes in them reveal where brave miners have dug. Perhaps this location is one of the more treacherous places to commute to work! Photograph courtesy of Jim Clanin.

Brice & Christophe GOBIN
www.mineralsweb.com

"If you don't know where you are going to,
look where you come from…"
(African saying)

Aquamarine, Fluorite, and Muscovite

Flying from Peshawar to the Northern Areas is a great experience. We are used to jumping on a plane to travel around the globe to find great mineral specimens, but the first time we took *that* flight was, for the very first time of our lives, well let's say it...*anxious*. In a Boeing 733 you are supposed to fly above anything on the planet, right? Well, here that is not so! The mountains are so high that you fly at the same height as the mountain tops! As you start descending, you pass along the Nanga Parbat summit (26,658 feet – 8,125 meters tall) which is higher than the plane. Then the plane starts to zig-zag between beautiful hills and valleys and then it maneuvers through a tight bend and at last to the narrow canyon that is the only access to Skardu airport. You jump out of the plane and before looking at the fantastic hills surrounding Skardu you think, "I'm still alive! Cool."

After a brief police control point at the airport, you are free. You look at these huge mountains around you, you feel so small, so fragile. At that point we were thinking that it wouldn't be a problem to come back from this trip without a rock. It was worth the trip to be here, to see: just to "feel". Those thoughts were good for us to have because, unfortunately, Skardu at that time wasn't the right place for great minerals. Anyway we thought, "We'll be back!"

On our next trip, we planned to go back to Skardu, but this time we wanted to also visit Gilgit and the Hunza Valley. A parcel of aquamarine and fluorite had just come out the week before and was waiting for us. "Nagar, here we come!" Chumar Bakhoor (Nagar Mine) is world famous for beautiful aquamarine crystals on muscovite and fantastic fluorites. Specimens rarely come with additional and desirable crystal associations on the same matrix.

On our way to Nagar village, we were dreaming about the piece we were supposed to see. Based on the news we had, Abdul Aziz and Mirwali, our friends in Pakistan, were convinced that this would be the "lucky trip". After a long talk, and many green teas, the parcel was unveiled. The pocket was better than we expected. What a surprise when we discovered, on the particular piece shown on the facing page, the matrix was the "Aqua"! And it was not a small one! It was a great one! - with a beautiful green fluorite attached on the front of the piece with some delicate muscovite crystals sparkling around.

We took the piece in our hands and turned it in every way as we were sure to find a problem somewhere, some damage, a scratch, an edge with a tiny ding, something that would have killed our excitement. Again and again we checked the aquamarine, the fluorite and the muscovite, but found no problem! "Is that possible? No matrix to protect the aqua or the fluorite, but there was not even a scratch?" We couldn't believe it.

Then our pulse increased as we asked the fateful question, "How much?" After a long and stormy discussion, we shook hands with the owner of the parcel. We grabbed the piece and carefully packed it; the treasure was now ours. After a wonderful dinner, a short night and a 20 hour drive back, we reached the Pearl Continental Hotel in Peshawar. A hot green tea was waiting for us in our room.

AQUAMARINE, Fluorite, and Muscovite
Nagar Mine, Hunza Valley, Pakistan

10.7 x 15 cm. Jeff Scovil photograph.

by Brice Gobin and Christophe Gob

TANZANITE
Merelani Hills, Foothills of Mount Kilimanjaro, Tanzania

6.2 cm high. Brice Gobin photograph

Tanzanite is one of our favorite minerals! We love it; the color, the shape, the luster, all are terrific! Since the discovery of the species Tanzanite, in 1967, Tanzania remains the only place on Earth to produce this beautiful blue-purple variety of zoisite.

The Merelani Hills, the remarkable location in the foothills of Mount Kilimanjaro, have been producing this fabulous gemstone nearly continuously for the last 40 years. We started to travel to Tanzania in 2008 as we wanted to add a new "string on our bow". We had some good contacts and friends there and we had a gap in our schedule of 10 days; so it was the right time for the jump! Africa is special and beautiful. The atmosphere, the ambiance, the odors, the people, everything is unique. We have been very active on the African continent since the late 1970s; it is always a great pleasure to discover a new place, a new country.

The first trip to a mineral area to see the suppliers is always very important. The local brokers and miners watch you closely. They all wonder what is your "taste", meaning what is your range, the money you can put on the table? So this is crucial; if you want to achieve here you must make a first good impression, that is imperative. We rejected a lot of material that was just rough for cutting, "crystal shapes", or "decoration pieces" as they call the mineral specimens. The miners and brokers were speechless and started to wonder if we were crazy; "These new buyers are not serious. They are just NOT buying?!?" Then we bought one piece, a single thumbnail, a beautiful, water clear deep blue jewel and I paid the price for it! The buzz was gone and we became the "muzungu" (meaning "white" in Swahili) who buy ONLY gem material in crystal shape !!

The tanzanite crystal in this gallery was offered to us, not so long ago and we think it is among the best tanzanite crystals ever found. It is flawless, unheated, undamaged, and glassy. The crystal had just fallen out of the graphite matrix during extraction and very few parts are missing from its base.

Tanzanite crystals on matrix are extremely rare, but this one is rare also, because it is essentially a complete crystal. Our best friend and supplier had called three days before, saying: "Hey Brice, you should come down to Tanzania, there is a nice crystal in town!" How correct he was. The feeling is always the same when you know you are going to see something special. - something desirable, something rare. You know it's here, in a box on the table, or in a safe behind the next door. You don't want to show your excitement, but you betray yourself as you drink your coffee or soda a bit too fast. You dreamed about it and traveled far to see it and the anticipation almost takes your breath away as the crystal is unveiled. We were very fortunate to be offered this piece and hope some day to have an opportunity to get another one like it.

This tourmaline is the kind of piece that you are happy to get and sad to sell, because you know it's unlikely that another specimen so good will come along any time soon. We got it directly in Peshawar, in the Namak Mandi stone market. Fortunately for us, the majority owner of this beautiful specimen is one of our very best friends in Peshawar and this is the reason why it is so important to make a good first impression when you enter a new market. If the key people involved in this market trust you, it is certain that you will get a phone call one day letting you know that there is something special and you should jump on a plane and have a look.

We got the call from our friend and we began bargaining right away. We didn't want to waste time as we "knew" the price was too high! But my friend convinced me to fly to Pakistan, to sit and drink 10 teas looking at this beautiful specimen. We though well maybe "We'll find some more good stuff around and whether we buy this tourmaline or not we can still make it a worthwhile trip." It took us three days to get it! - two hours per day of negotiation and loud talking between our two friends and with all of the partners involved in this piece. (Most of the big parcels and high-end mineral specimens belong to many different persons to reduce the risk of loss of money, if the piece does not sell at the right price.) The piece was "sealed" three times for us, as they are used to packing it back, taping it, and signing on it to prove that the piece is still under negotiation and no one else can buy it at that stage!

We were, of course, very happy and proud to succeed here as we think this is one of the nicest bi-colored tourmaline from Paprok ever found. The balance of the piece is great, the tourmaline is gorgeous pink to a vivid green with gemmy areas on a white albite and a sharp smoky quartz on the side. It made our day of course and made a customer friend's day, soon after, in Tucson.

TOURMALINE, Quartz, and Albite
Paprok Mine, Nuristan, Afghanistan

10.3 cm wide. Jeff Scovil photograph

VANADINITE
Mibladen mine, Midelt, Morocco

10.3 cm wide. Brice Gobin photograph.

Vanadinite

Morocco! - what a beautiful country, such a contrasted place! When traveling from north to south you pass from a pure Mediterranean landscape, with eucalyptus trees, pine trees, olive trees, and flowers … to mountains covered with snow and then directly to the desert! The gateway town to enter into the desert is Ouarzazate.

Normally, the drive from Marrakech to Ouarzazate should take about 4 hours. You have to climb up to the Tischka Pass and get down to the other side of the hill. However, if Christophe is driving it will take much less time, but you will miss all the fantastic views, valleys, the typical villages with kids playing along the road, riding donkeys or selling fake and glued geodes of quartz with fancy blue, gold or even rainbow colors! The scenery is truly breath-taking.

A friend had the good idea to join us this time for the trip. We think he will never forget it! Christophe couldn't pass Ouarzazate without visiting some of our friends dealing in top quality minerals from Bou Azzer. This famous mine is producing the best erythrites in the world and some beautiful cobaltoan calcites as well. Unfortunately, this time the luck seemed to be only on the roadside. Time was slipping away and Christophe had to rush to Midelt, there was a new stunning lot of 100 top red vanadinites that had just come out from the famous Mibladen Mine. Passing downtown Midelt City, he recognized some fellows and miners at the main" tea café", outside on the sunny terrace: "No time for a mint tea, was his thought - Later!" He arrived in Mibladene in a kind of "Paris-Dakar desert race" style, with a huge cloud of dust behind his car, and our friend, hanging on, could at last breath

What is better than a fresh mint tea to chill down and relax after such a bumpy drive? A mint tea and a great lot of "vanas" (vanadinites), of course! The vanas were very fine, very red, very bright…very expensive…5 pieces were immediately located in the parcel. The specimen shown on the facing page wasn't the biggest, but it was, by far, the finest. The one pictured is "la crème de la crème" of this lot - superb! The pocket came out in the old and very famous Acif Vein in the Mibladen Mine. That's the only lode in the Mibladene area that produces such beautiful big red crystals of vanadinite. Christophe was facing a price problem as the owners of this lot had overpriced the entire parcel. The 5 pieces that he pointed out were the key specimens there and Christophe wouldn't give up. "We need that piece!" he told his brother on the phone! After a long discussion, he got them at last. A month after the 5 pieces had found a warm and safe place in private collections.

Beside those beautiful 5 pieces, the market was empty in Midelt and it was time to head back to Marrakech for a delicious and spicy little snail soup and a superb lamb kebab plate, on the very famous and smoky (due to dozens of barbecues) Jeema-El-Fna square. Needless to say, with five beautiful and valuable vanas in the car, the way back to Marrakech was pure pleasure. Every evening this place is transformed into a huge outdoor restaurant. There are king cobra snakes dancing from the rhythm of the Arabic flutes, vendors selling hats," baboushs" (Arabian shoes), and beautiful potteries. There are also small shopkeepers squeezing fresh oranges for juice. This is a wonderful experience for anyone who wants to immerse themselves into the blood of this incredible town. If you're go one day in Morocco, don't miss it! This place is unique!

Topaz, Schorl, Fluorite, and Cleavelandite

When you fly to a source for minerals, you never know what's going to happen and what you are going to find. Most of the time, we metaphorically go "fishing in the deep blue sea with no sign of life in it", but we always hope to catch the "big red tuna"! Sometimes we've heard that, the day before, lots of birds were seen in the Ligurian sea of the Mediterranean. So…, we take our chances and we head to the place. Suddenly our rod bangs and the reel spins. Action! Mineral hunting is almost the same. You never know when you will "hit" a killer rock, you'll never expect it! You may have always dreamt about it. You may have drawn it dozens of times in your mind, but nothing like it ever actually comes to you. Once in a while, there is the good news. In Peshawar, I saw this beautiful piece. My surprise was enormous and was completely unexpected. When you know something is coming to you, you hope the piece is going to be good. Just as the story tells, "Time goes in slow motion… Don't even think about it, because if you do, you're going to be very disappointed!" I had heard about a piece that had been found 4 or 5 days before and it was coming by road from the Haramosh mine (Northern Pakistan). "A major piece!" my Pakistani friend was telling me on the phone. I was told it was a very special combination of black tourmaline and topaz. My contact arrived in town after a 24-hour trip on the road. As I was feeling his smile behind his long beard, I was getting very excited to see the stone, but long minutes were passing, so long… In Pakistan, like in most of the Islamic countries, you have to welcome a guest with a cup of tea or any drink or food, before starting any business. He was our guest in our office in Peshawar. we couldn't avoid tradition. We were excited and thirsty, so at least one cup of tea chilled us down! When this topaz with schorl specimen was revealed to us, we were at first shocked by the overall size of the piece (20.5 cm long) and by the contrast between the black of the double terminated tourmaline and the white of the cleavelandite - and it was a floater! The most important aspect of this piece is of course the topaz. The topaz is a clean 5 cm crystal, that could have been anywhere on this piece, but for some reason and that's what makes it so special, it "decided" to grow here, on the top right position of the tourmaline, attached to the albite, which put this piece in an ultimate level of quality and beauty. All the species represented in our gallery are of a very high standard and this specimen's aesthetic display makes it extremely special and desirable. It is like a cherry on the cake. The wonderful topaz is attached to the black tourmaline; there is a little green fluorite cube, and a second small topaz. As we gently turned the piece, we meticulously inspected it. Sometimes the beauty and the quality of a piece are like rays of light in your eyes and make you miss a small ding or an even bigger problem. Of course, the piece was damage-free and our excitement was high. The feeling at that point is hard to explain to the people who don't understand our hobby. After a long (very long) talk and many cups of tea, the topaz was proudly ours. we surmise in all levels of people involved in our business, from the miner who goes 500 meters deep underground or climbs 4000 meters up in the mountains, to the dealer that flies to these difficult regions, or to the collector who spends money to get the ultimate piece, we all take a risk in a certain way, but this is because of Passion.
"Life is a risk. If you did not risk, you did not live. ... risk gives a … special Champagne."
– Sister Emanuelle

BERYL Variety MORGANITE
Corrego do Urucum, Minas Gerais, Brazil

7.5 cm wide. Jeff Scovil photograph.

Morganite

Morganite is the pink variety of beryl named in 1911 by George F. Kunz in honor of John Pierpont Morgan, a rich banker, benefactor, and collector of minerals and gemstones. Pure beryl is colorless and it is sometimes called "goshenite." However, on account of its crystal form, beryl may contain foreign elements such as iron, manganese, chromium, or vanadium. If manganese is present in beryl, the rather plain, colorless gemstone becomes a beautiful pink color, Morganite. For us, the shape is very important of course, but we think the key for a good morganite is the color. We like the pink to be truly PINK! - not orange pink or barely pink.

We got this piece from a very fine collection some years ago. We were working to acquire that collection for a very long time and it was quite difficult to get access to it. Sometimes, we thought that it would be *easier* to go at the end of the world, where laws do not exist; with just sardines in a box for your meal and a "minus 3 stars" hotel to sleep in, to get the ultimate piece. Well, our only consolation is that it is good for collectors to know what treasures they have and it is understandable that they are reluctant to sell them. Everyone should realize what trials and tribulations accompany the acquisition of a gemstone or mineral specimen at the source.

Although we bought this specimen from a mineral collector, we know that specimen acquisition is not always so easy. When we got the "green light" from the mineral collector to visit his collection, we don't ordinarily expect to get such a fine example. This crystal may be justifiably called a "killer" morganite! It is not a simple one, it's a complete, very well formed, glassy and extremely gemmy morganite crystal. After a proper cleaning process, the back of the piece happened to be of the same luster and quality as the front side. This undamaged, complete floater crystal is one of the best known in the world.

I think that Africa teaches the travails of the specimen's journey to market very well. The African miner has to solve tons of different kinds of problems, even before making a first hole in the ground. He has first to find money to give to his family, as he is leaving the village for several weeks. Once he arrives to the village where the mine site is located, he must meet with the chief of the village and negotiate to stay there and to work. If he gets lucky, he can start immediately working in the pit. Unfortunately, some militaries have heard about this guy, with a little money, working at the mine with a small team. Soon, they arrive for their "cut". Luckily, the miner "heats" a pocket with few insignificant pieces of gemstones or crystals. But he still has big problems. "Don't worry everyone will get a piece of the cake"; but not just only for those who sweated for it.

A mine is rarely next to a road. A beautiful stone has, most of the time, been hand dug and hand carried out of the mine, then packed in banana leaves, tightened up on the back of a bicycle and shaken up on a bumpy dirt road during a 50 kilometer ride. Then, dropped on a truck with 50 other people, chickens, coal bags, corn, manioc roots and plenty of other stuff piled up on top of everyone; then packed and unpacked each time a military check point is crossed, with a little "contribution" taken each time. If the miner gets really lucky, the specimen is still in one piece and not two and safely reaches a town. If someone like us is around and if we like it, we may buy it. So long may be the route to the "green light."

by Brice Gobin and Christophe Gobin   110

Chapter Three: *Thirty Five Years of Refining*
by Mario Pauwels

I was born in 1964 in Belgium and live in Flanders, the northern and Dutch speaking part of Belgium. By age ten, I had started collecting minerals and was fortunate that my parents were supportive of my hobby and would take me on field collecting trips and to mineral shows in Belgium and Germany. It was exciting to discover that minerals could be so colorful and that crystals could develop into so many different shapes. Over  Thirty-five years later, my collecting philosophy has become more focused, but the basic truths remain the same. The visual aesthetics and quality of the specimen must immediately attract me. Even as a young collector I always sought the best specimens my limited funds would allow. The elements that are important to me include pleasing crystal form, color, interesting associations, freedom of damage or repair, and gem crystals. There is only one repaired specimen in my collection at this time; a very fine tourmaline on matrix that never could have survived the mining operations intact. I could not resist the beauty of this specimen and I felt compelled to make the purchase. I understand that repairs are widely accepted, but they still bother me in most cases. Travel is important. The collector has to be where the minerals are. Having made more than sixty trips thus far to North and South America, not to mention my native Europe, mineral specimens from many countries are very well represented in the collection. Years ago after a visit to my first major mineral show, I decided to reduce the size of my collection and focus on upgrading its quality. To that end I started participating as a dealer at mineral shows. These days I do only a few shows a year as a mineral dealer; but I am a very passionate collector and I can be found at all the major American and European mineral shows. At the present time, my collection contains about 280 mineral specimens and gem crystals of various sizes. Quality and aesthetics reign, not the size of the specimens nor the size of the collection. I have no ambition to build a collection of thousands of pieces. I wish to keep a concise collection of superb minerals and gems that can be displayed beautifully. I also have no illusions that my criteria would satisfy every collector. Collections reflect the preferences of the individual. I believe that anyone can build a very fine collection with modest funds; great wealth is not requisite to the enjoyment of mineral collecting. The key is to develop a certain taste for fine specimens and to search prudently and patiently.

Mario Pauwels

People ask me "How I learn about minerals?" There is no substitute for personally looking at minerals. Museums and major mineral shows provide great opportunity to study and compare the quality of minerals. I read books and subscribe to periodicals. Magazines such as the *Mineralogical Record, Mineral Up, Rocks and Minerals,* and others are invaluable resources for collectors. I am proud to be the first European member of the Mineralogical Record Fellow program. Magazines provide both contemporary and historical perspective and detailed information that assist in the development of a more comprehensive bank of knowledge to draw upon when considering minerals. Over the decades, I have had the privilege of meeting many dealers, collectors, miners and field collectors while visiting miners, mines, and shows searching for minerals and I have a reservoir of precious memories of those people, travels, and experiences. The reward of being allowed to acquire extraordinary minerals is worth all of the effort and certainly those fine pieces do not mean less to me because I did not always move the dirt and rock to collect them. Realistically, the only way to build a fine worldwide mineral collection is to purchase them; it is virtually impossible to personally collect a comprehensive aesthetic collection as the marketplace holds the treasures of literally tens of thousands of individuals. Mineral collecting is a wonderful hobby. It can be done over a lifetime, alone or with others; whether the budget is large or small, a display that satisfies the collector can be developed. From the beginning to the end, a mineral collector always has something interesting to consider and beauty to admire. It is a very fine experience.

Gold
Idaho Pit, The Golden Mile District, Kalgoorlie-Boulder, Western Australia, Australia

The Golden Mile District is one of the world's greatest gold deposits. This gold was the last mineral to form in a cavity already lined with quartz and ankerite crystals that are the common gangue minerals in the Golden Mile lodes. The rhombic and hexagonal impressions in the gold were made by these original crystals. The base of the gold was in direct contact with the crystal-lined wall of the vug, while the upper side had areas that were free-growing and in the open space lustrous rounded complex gold crystals were able to form. This specimen is reputedly the best gold ever found in the district. 9.7 x 9.5 x 3.2 cm, 815 grams. Specimen was found in April 2007. F. Van Mieghem photograph.

Tourmaline on a Quartz floater
Escondido Mine, Golconda, Minas Gerais, Brazil.

Remarkable fragile green "pencils" of tourmaline on a complete quartz crystal group. 8.2 x 2.9 cm. Jeff Scovil photograph.

Tourmaline on Cleavelandite
Afghan Pocket, Pederneira Mine, Minas Gerais, Brazil.

Outstanding polychrome tourmaline on a bed of white cleavelandite blades. 17.5 x 10 x 7.5 cm. Joaquim Callén photograph.

Smithsonite
Kelly Mine, Socorro County, New Mexico, U.S.A.

Smithsonite is a beautiful mineral that may be found in a variety of colors. Teal, however, is a rare enough color for this species to make a good specimen of it an important acquisition for the connoisseur mineral collector and the Kelly Mine is known for its "top shelf" specimens. This specimen is particularly attractive for its bubbly surface that catches light from many angles. Back lighting reveals its ocean water quality. 9.3 x 6.5 cm. F. Van Mieghem photograph.

**Morganite - Apatite - Quartz - Cleavelandite
Paprok Mine, Pech, Kunar Valley, Afghanistan.**

Occasionally very fine minerals have an unexpected "touch", where the placement of a companion mineral provides a wonderful aesthetic result. This pink morganite beryl is gemmy, well-formed, and well-placed. The flanking quartz crystals are nice. The open-spaced white cleavelandite blades are a further complement. The lilac ribbon of apatite, however, magnifies what is already a great specimen. The playful diagonal of the apatite ribbon suggest a favorite book with a place marked or the tassel on a graduate's mortar board. There is no other specimen like this one. 13.8 x 11.6 x 6.5 cm. Jeff Scovil photograph.

Epidote with Adularia
Tormiq Valley, Skardu Road, Haramosh Mountains, Gilgit, Pakistan

The specimen is a completely-formed floater and has the same "great looks" on front and back. It is very impressive because of the big size for the species, the very solid look, and the high luster. The combination with the white adularia penetrating straight through the dark olive brown epidote makes this specimen important, but the added feature of a parallel grid of the epidote growth is another of Nature's gifts. The specimen was found in the spring of 2009. 19 x 11.7 x 4.4 cm. F. Van Mieghem photograph.

Fluorite on Fluorite
Minerva # 1 Mine, Cave-in-Rock District, Illinois, U.S.A.

Fluorite is a widely-occurring mineral and its colors and forms may be wonderful. This combination of yellow and pale blue fluorite is characteristic of the Cave-in-Rock District, but the overgrowth of the blue crystal on the etched yellow core is the kind of specimen mineral collectors yearn for. 11.6 x 7.1 cm. F. Van Mieghem photograph.

Amethyst
Piedra Parada Mine, Las Vigas, Vera Cruz, Mexico

This lovely specimen is a flower unlike the many thousands of it kind. Van Mieghem photograph. 12.8 x 10.8 x 10 cm - cluster: 8.8 x 8.5 x 6.3 cm. Ex Keith Proctor Collection. F. Van Mieghem photograph.

Spodumene - Kunzite
Resplendor Mine, Minas Gerais, Brazil

This specimen was almost another one that "got away". Neither pink spodumene (kunzite) nor mint green spodumene are difficult to acquire, but this combination of colors in scepter-like overgrowth is unique and would be a major piece in any collection. Ex Keith Proctor Collection. 19 x 6.2 cm. F. Van Mieghem photograph.

Gold "Ram's Horn"
Butte Creek, Paradise, Plumas County, California, U.S.A.

Ram's Horn gold is a target mineral for many mineral collectors. Although the specimens with maximum "curly-cue" development are the most highly prized, even specimens with gentle curves are desirable. This is a specimen found in a placer in the 1960s. 10.1 x 1.5 cm. 175 grams. Jeff Scovil photograph.

Mimetite
Congresso-Leon Mine, San Pedro Corralitos, Chihuahua, Mexico

Crystal form is not the only desirable aspect of a fine mineral specimen. Mimetite is often found in gorgeous brightly colored botryoidal specimens. The Congresso Leon Mine is noted for its exceptionally choice mimetite. The surface of the botryoids has a satiny luster where light glints off from microscopic crystal faces that are tightly intergrown. The overall grouping of the minute crystals is responsible for the rounded shapes. While minerals may be any color, excellent yellow minerals are scarce. This mimetite was found in 1969. 8.2 x 5 cm.
F. Van Mieghem photograph.

However you have come to this volume, Paradise Woods would like to thank you for having the interest and taking the time to examine the contents. We share your excitement in the quest for the quintessential mineral specimen and the pride in ownership which has moved mineral collectors through the ages. Hopefully within these pages there is something to bring some bit of that excitement out in you and in doing so help perpetuate and grow our hobby.

Schorl on Cleavelandite
Shengus, Skardu Road, Gilgit, Pakistan

Schorl is the most common of the tourmaline species, but it is very under-represented in museums, because black tourmalines are usually found encased in rock. Schorl seldom has well-formed faces and because it is enclosed in rock, the crystals are rarely freed without severe damage. The premiere locality for black tourmaline crystals is Pakistan. This 9.5 cm tall schorl crystal is embraced by a feathery cluster of cleavelandite crystals. An unobtrusive clear quartz crystal completes a trio of crystallized "common" minerals. Joaquim Callén photograph.

Purple Apatite
Pulsifer Quarry, Auburn
Androscoggin County, Maine, USA

Purple Apatite is known as "Queen of the Phosphates" with good reason. Her beauty, shapes, mineral associations, and color varieties are almost unmatched among the minerals. Purple apatite is widespread in the world, but the world's best crystals are still from Pitt Pulsifer's quarry first opened about 1900. In 1966, this locality was re-opened and this remarkable crystal was found. The intense purple color is due to high valance manganese as a trace enrichment. The fascinating apatites of the Pulsifer Quarry are also wonderfully rich in rare faces and textures further enhancing their world-class status. 3.5 cm wide. Illustrated in American Mineral treasures, p. 342. Joaquim Callén photograph.

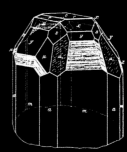

Drawings from

Wolff and Palache (1902).

Fluorite
Okorusu Fluorspar Mine, Otjiwarongo District, Namibia

This is a common mineral with uncommon qualities: bright crimson to dark mauve color zones interspersed in a cubic crystal cluster (7.6 cm tall). The specimen has several exciting features. Firstly the color zones indicate a change in growth direction of the fluorite. The color phantoms are now oriented at 45 degrees to the final growth edges. The multiple steps of terminations indicate rapid advancement in face growth as the pathway of crystallization rapidly changed. The unique placement of the main crystal in a host of similar smaller crystals is stunning. Joaquim Callén photograph.

Rhodonite
Morro da Mina Mine, Conselheiro Lafaiete, Minas Gerais, Brazil

Magnificent terminated rhodonite crystal from one of the world's greatest finds. This 5.1cm tall crystal is without matrix and stands perfectly displaying its exceptionally well-formed features. Highlights reveal excellent striations while back-lighting shows the gemminess and intensity of color. When these bright red crystals were discovered in a sooty black manganese mine, initial tests suggested that these were an entirely new species to the world. Despite their subsequent traditional species determination, they are beautiful. 5.1 cm wide.
Joaquim Callén photograph.

Amethyst
Deer Hill, Stow, Oxford County, Maine, USA

A mineral may be a variety of a mineral species, but on rare occasions, it may be two varieties. Parallel growth quartz and amethyst quartz are two varieties, and on occasion a specimen may be both. Deer Hill has produced quartz with either one variety or the other, and not too rarely both, but this specimen not only outshines its locality brethren, it holds a place in the world's parallel growth amethyst Hall of Fame. 11.3 cm tall. Joaquim Callén photograph.

Azurite and Malachite
Luifengshan Mine, Chizho Prefecture,
Anhui Province, China

Green and blue minerals in high quality, associated together, is a prized combination. Historically, there have been few localities, which have yielded good malachite with good azurite. The most famous location is in Bisbee, Arizona, USA, but its heyday of production is long since past. Today, there is another brief opportunity to obtain similar specimens, but that opportunity will likely soon fade away as well. This 12.7 cm tall specimen features a midnight blue drusy azurite field with green feathery malachite. Joaquim Callén photograph.

Chapter Five. *Elmwood Mine Minerals, Tennessee*
by Dr. Steve Neely

I was born in 1945 with a fully expressed "collector gene". As a young child I collected marbles followed by baseball cards and comics. As an early teenager, numismatics and philately became my prime interest. The one overriding principle of these early collections was always to obtain the very best example available that was within budgetary constraints. As a late teenager, my collector gene took a back seat and actually became masked as other interests became my life focus: education, fast cars, motorcycles, and girls, in no particular order. Twenty years later, philately became again my dominant collection. In 1967, I signed up to take a geology course in my pre-med years and was told by my physician advisor that geology was a waste of time and money (the pervasive tunnel vision of a pre-med curriculum) and was instead encouraged (actually told) to take histochemistry. Well, 15 years later I was given a geology textbook by a grateful parent of an intern and my geology education was underway.

Steve Neely

In 1980, I moved to Tennessee and a few years later married a local lady from Carthage, Tennessee. As my orthopaedic practice began, I found myself taking care of real life miners from a zinc mine in Smith County. This was during the heyday of early mineral production and the miners would often bring a "thank you" gift to the office-- peculiar golden footballs, odd purple cubes, all on shiny black crystals with occasional white snowballs. The original decline at the Gordonsville Mine was on the farm of my wife's grandparents. Betty Lou and I developed a quick fascination with the minerals of Elmwood. Soon the miners learned there was a doctor in Lebanon, Tennessee, who paid cash money for their minerals. Circumstances grew in the favor of minerals and we were privileged to participate in the official mine auctions. Dr. Tim Thornhill (now deceased) was a long time collector, and he and I bid on lots together, brought them to my house, flipped a coin and then the fun of choosing began. Some of these will be shown in the ensuing picture gallery.

The fascination with the Elmwood minerals at times grew into an obsession, which according to my wife, Betty Lou, required a reality check. Our interests expanded to worldwide specimens and our education was accelerated by many collectors and dealers who today are dear friends such as Ralph Clark, Russ Behnke, Bruce Oreck, Bryan Lees, Keith Proctor, Marshall Sussman, and so many more. One evening in the mid 80s, Keith and I sat in a McDonald's for dinner after a trip to Mount Antero, Colorado and I hurriedly wrote down the 15 characteristics that make a great mineral specimen on several napkins. These remain today the criteria by which we evaluate specimens. We have refined these lessons and today will illustrate specimens from our Elmwood suite which contains about 200 examples. Not all we have acquired are the "best", some are pieces that are just our favorites. We will show various examples of the Elmwood mineralogy, both common and uncommon. Some of these photos will be familiar and some are pictured here for the first time. We hope these photos serve to expand ones appreciation for this great mineral producing locality. The author wishes to acknowledge several people without whose help and encouragement this Elmwood collection could not have been assembled: Walt Gaylord, Mary and Gary West, Jimmy Roberts and Jeff Langford.

Calcite and Fluorite

This is an immense 35.5 cm long "monster" calcite specimen. The "tiny" fluorite at the base is 5 cm and is perfect. The orange amber calcite is transparent on the two ends for over a distance of about 7.5 cm. The thick central section could not reasonably be transparent, but has to be translucent. I have personally never seen a better or more impressive calcite from Elmwood. This specimen was mined in the 1980s. "We" all heard about this great piece, but no one saw it and we dismissed it as "miners lore". Then 3 years ago. I went to visit one of my friends who was a miner and there was this specimen sitting alone in the center of the dining room table. I immediately recognized the piece as the one which we had never seen, but which we had heard about from so long ago. It is absolutely flawless sitting on a dolomite pedestal with a 5 cm fluorite. It is one of my favorite mineral specimens of all time.
Steve Neely photograph.

Celestine

Remarkable white fibrous celestine crystals in overlapping brushes from one of the few known finds in the Elmwood District. By any standard, fibrous sprays of celestine are unusual. Chemical analyses verify that the ratio of strontium to barium averages 2.5:1. The matrix is sphalerite and barite on dolomite. Gordonsville Mine. 10 x 10 cm. Steve Neely photograph.

Fluorite

Elmwood fluorite comes in a variety of colors and the true collector will have to have every variety possible. This particular fluorite has an unusual muted London-blue tint. The white barite and dolomite matrix with dark brown sphalerite crystals successfully provide the contrast for an interesting specimen. The two major fluorite crystals are the same size although the lower one has a clear corner. 10.8 x 14.3 cm. Jeff Scovil photograph.

Fluorite

Large fluorite crystals are rarely colorful, so when this specimen was available, it required little time to fall in love with it. The fluorite, itself, is a multiple growth. It is a full 12.5 cm on an edge and is sheathed by a rose purple exterior. However, the clear corner is a window into the orange interior. Dolomite on the left and bright, well-crystallized sphalerite on the right grip the specimen firmly. 17.8 x 20.3 cm. Jeff Scovil photograph.

Calcite Twin

Gem golden yellow calcite twin (10 cm) in a 7.5 x 10 cm crystal cluster. Calcite specimens of this quality are rare worldwide. The natural calcite crystal base immediately heightens the appearance of the main crystal. The orange tips of this calcite and the prominent twin girdle of the calcite as well as its remarkably fortuitous placement is an inspiration for calcites every-where. Exhibited in the *American Mineral Treasures* case at Tucson. Jeff Scovil photograph.

Calcite twin

Large golden calcite twin (12.5 cm tall) with creamy white barite. One of the allures of Elmwood minerals is their great size and this specimen has that quality *par excellence.* The specimen displays well with the twin girdle prominently placed. The transparent, rich golden amber terminations are nicely accented by the clear calcite crystals on the side and creamy white barite below. Specimen is 15 x 16 cm. Jeff Scovil photograph.

Fluorite

The Elmwood Mine is renowned for having produced etched "corners" of fluorite. The main section of this etched light purple fluorite is sugary textured with a gemmy colorless spike fluorite core that formerly extended from the corner of a cube to the very center of the crystal. The image has an optical illusion where the spike projecting to the upper right is counter-balanced by the dark edges of the fluorite cube showing from the far back interior of the transparent core. This piece is unusual even for this occurrence and very few specimens such as this one were recovered. 7.5 x 7.5 cm with 4 cm spike. Jeff Scovil photograph.

Fluorite on Sphalerite

Pale purple fluorite crystal with clear corners and multiple stepped texture on the central areas of the faces. A 2 cm gem calcite crystal extends out on the right side of the fluorite. The dark brown sphalerite crystal matrix also shows multiple-growth of faces. The simple description does not reveal the passion this specimen displays. The transition of purples coupled with the subtle color bands on the corners insist that this is a major specimen. Specimen is 6 by 8 cm and the fluorite crystal is 4.1 cm on an edge. Jeff Scovil photograph.

Fluorite and Galena

Gem rose purple fluorite on galena. The galena parallels the development of the fluorite crystals as it too shows multiple stepped faces. I'm particularly attracted to the interplay between the blue purple and the red purple fluorite crystals, while metallic gray galena provides the perfect association. 16.5 by 17.5 cm. Jeff Scovil photograph.

Fluorite

Purple fluorite crystal (5 cm) with typical stepped parquet texture on dolomite crystals. This is a well-placed fluorite crystal on interestingly textured, dolomite crystal-sprinkled matrix (10 cm long). If there were only one Elmwood fluorite chosen to represent the characteristics of the Elmwood locality, many would think of this specimen as the one.

Jeff Scovil photograph.

Fluorite

Rose purple fluorite with multiple stepped crystal growth on sphalerite. This is a literal as well as figurative giant among fluorite crystals. Images in a book have a tendency to make all specimens appear to be the same size, but size does matter in a great display specimen. 19 cm by 23.5 cm. The fluorite crystal is 13.5 cm on edge. Exhibited in the *American Mineral Treasures* case at Tucson. Illustrated in the book, *American Mineral Treasures*.
Jeff Scovil photograph.

Fluorite on Sphalerite

Although Elmwood fluorite crystals can be very large, they can also be delicately colored. This pinkish purple cube has an interior yellow glow when well-lighted. Additionally, the clear corners have a smooth surface that abruptly steps up to a textured field seemingly reminiscent of a theatrical curtain rising to reveal the stage behind. Dark brown sphalerite crystals rest in the "orchestra". 7 x 7.9 cm. Jeff Scovil photograph.

Calcite Twins

In many ways, this is an astonishing specimen. The main crystal is a full 27.5 cm long and came out of the 40-14 South Section, Cumberland Shaft of the Elmwood Mine. Because of these crystals' enormity, they are also deeply amber colored with an orange tint. The symmetry of these crystals is well-displayed showing nearly perfect scalenohedral faces while the twinning is equally spectacular. This specimen was featured in *American Mineral Treasures*, but was far too over-powering to display with other Elmwood specimens in the *American Mineral Treasures* exhibit case. Illustrated in *Mineralogical Record,* volume 33 #1, page 84, 2002. Jeff Scovil photograph.

by Steve Neely   142

Fluorite

Four purple parquet-surface fluorite cubes on dolomite. Specimen is 7.5 x 10.5 cm with each cubic crystal over 3 cm on an edge. Exhibited in the *American Mineral Treasures* case at Tucson. Illustrated in *extraLapis: Fluorite the Collector's Choice.* page 54, 2006.
Jeff Scovil photograph.

Fluorite

The Elmwood Mine produced many giant crystals, but it was always a treat to see a *beautiful* giant fluorite. The rose purple to somewhat amber purple of the interior glow is a delight. One of the charms of this specimen is that it isn't perfect. The interior shows nascent fractures that have rectangular patterns adjacent to triangles. The juxtaposition of a second fluorite with both on sphalerite enhances the appreciation of the specimen. Featured on the cover of the Jersey Meniere 1991 calender. Exhibited in the *American Mineral Treasures* case at Tucson. 11.4 x 14 cm. Jeff Scovil photograph.

Fluorite

This is a truly pleasant specimen. The fluorite crystal is canted on matrix at just the right angle. The faces are uncommonly smooth for an Elmwood specimen and the deep purple color zone is just the right distance from the crystal edges. The dark shadow of the crystal's interior belies the gemminess of the mineral. This specimen "competes" very well with color-zoned fluorite specimens of the world. 4.4 x 4.4 cm. Jeff Scovil photograph.

Fluorite

Multiple fluorite spikes within a color zoned cubic fluorite crystal. While the process of forming gemmy clear spiked etched fluorite corners and cores has been debated and theorized, their marvelous nature is undisputed. The concentric character of the various features of this specimen including the central snow-like texture in the specimen's center, is provocative. 8.9 x 15.9 cm. Jeff Scovil photograph.

Barite and Fluorite

Holding with the theme of giants among their kind is this beautiful purple "Stairway to the Stars". Each deep purple fluorite crystal is 7.5 cm on an edge and shows the glints of reflected light of the growth features of the faces. The creamy white spherical clusters of barite tightly frame this exceptional specimen. 19 x 33.7 cm. Jeff Scovil photograph.

Fluorite on Galena

When I am asked what I feel my favorite Elmwood specimen is, I immediately talk about this specimen. Many collectors seem to prefer color as their main reason for appreciating a mineral. For me, this combination of two lightly color-accented, embracing cubes on bright metallic gray galena crystals from the Stonewall Heading of the Elmwood Mine is aesthetic. One other, but smaller, specimen was found like this one, but it crumbled to pieces when the miners were attempting to recover it. 22 x 24 cm. Jeff Scovil photograph.

by Steve Neely   148

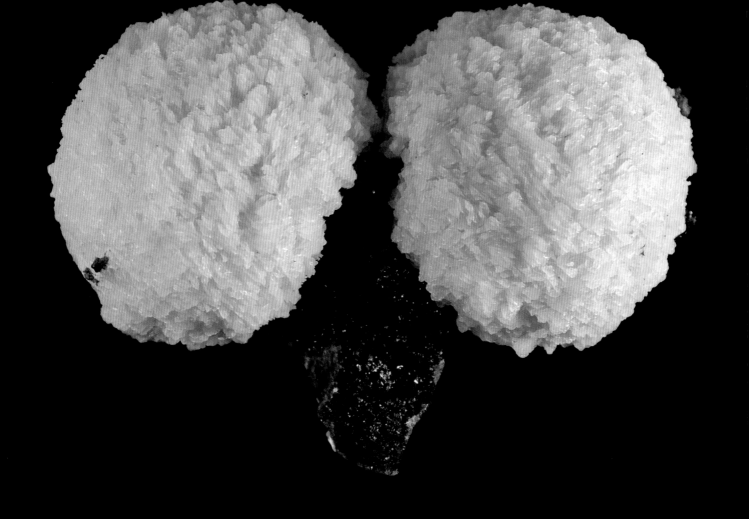

Barite

Two large, balanced spherical clusters of creamy white barite crystals on a triangular dark brown sphalerite stalk. This is a simple combination, but one which has rare aesthetic qualities. Elmwood is famous for its spherical barite clusters, but this combination with large size and balance made it a treasure. 21.5 cm wide. Steve Neely photograph.

Calcite on Fluorite

As collectors, we try to obtain the "ultimate" specimen. When we first saw this piece, we immediately recognized that this specimen was"it", but it would be many years before we could acquire it. The crystal was originally found by a lady miner. A female miner is a great rarity in the mining industry as unwarranted superstition kept mining male-dominated throughout history until only the last few decades. The specimen is not a huge one, but is unique because it shows the extreme etching of a fluorite crystal followed by a beautiful calcite crystal formed in just the right place. It was carefully wrapped in a kerchief and brought into the light of day. 3.5 x 4.4 cm. Jeff Scovil photograph.

Wayne can't pinpoint an exact time when his interest in the California gold rush began. He can, however, point to Mrs. Kirkby at the Jurupa Nature Center for stimulating his mineral collecting passions in the third grade. She made a visit to his grade school class and brought some minerals found in the nearby hills that were dotted with pegmatite formations. He was hooked and would often be scolded by his teacher for drifting off to those nearby hills to dig.

His grandfather had a cabin in Toulumene Meadows where he spent many summers there panning for gold and just taking in the history of the California gold rush. Always in the back of his mind during his 'growing up' years and throughout his years as an Army Intelligence officer and career in low temperature physics research; the 'fever' finally emerged when KRISTALLE was officially established in 1971.

Wayne and Dona Leicht

Kristalle's first location was in a small retail-shopping plaza in Laguna Beach, California. Wayne continued to work at his job at Aeronutronic (a division of Ford Motor Company) in Newport Beach and Dona worked in the gallery during the week. On weekends Wayne helped out at the Kristalle store. This plunge into the mineral business could not have happened had it not been for a friendship forged with the late Paul Desautels (former curator at the Smithsonian). Paul invited Wayne to join him on an 'around the world' trip where he introduced Wayne to the many curators, collectors, dealers from many countries. Paul convinced us that we would be good mineral dealers and would be happy doing it. It took sometime for us to also come to that conclusion. "To give up the nice paycheck, the supplied car, the stock options, medical, paid vacations to enter a business selling something that no one really needs – they just have to want it!!! After a couple of years into the business in Laguna Beach, we finally made it our full-time occupation. Our very first show was the "Pasadena" show sponsored by the Mineralogical Society of Southern California (Wayne was also president of the society for a number of years) and Pasadena was followed by shows in Bisbee, Arizona (so much fun in the early days), Detroit, and Tucson where we held forth in the old Desert Inn until gaining a berth at the TGMS show.

Over the 40 years of the KRISTALLE enterprise we have handled over 150 collections of minerals and gold. Certainly the collection that began our specialty of offering gold specimens was the famous Charles Crespi collection of Angels Camp, California. Several specimens in that broad collection have become 'world famous' including one, which we kept for our own small collection: the so-called "tree root" specimen from the Red Ledge Mine in California. This specimen was formed close to the surface and the gold formed around a tree root, which is still lodged in the middle of the specimen. Another specimen, referred to as the "seaweed" gold, is housed at the Smithsonian and on prominent display. For over 25 years, we have worked with the owner of the Eagle's Nest Mine in Placer County which, until recently, has consistently produced fine crystallized gold specimens that are now sprinkled around the world in museums and private collections. Some years ago, we also purchased another famous gold collection: the Segerstrom gold collection which was on display for many years at the U.S. Mint in San Francisco. Wayne's interest in the history of the California Gold Rush extended into building a personal collection of early maps, books, letters, photos, and ephemera that is now considered one of the most extensive in the country. We have loaned our personal gold collection and artifacts to many museums around the world for special displays, including the giant sesquicentennial display for the State of California in honor of the 150-year anniversary of the 1848 gold find in California. Los Angeles County Museum, Houston Museum, Bowers Museum, San Diego Natural History Museum, the French National Museum and Bonn University have also exhibited our specimens.

We have traveled the world in search of specimens with trips to Sri Lanka, India, Africa, South America, Colombia, Peru, Australia and throughout Europe. Our show schedule has expanded to include shows in the United States (Costa Mesa, Houston, San Francisco, Springfield, Tucson and Denver) and overseas in Tokyo, Munich, St. Marie aux Mines and England. Our gallery has also expanded – 15 years ago we purchased our own historic building on the main highway in Laguna Beach.

Dona and Wayne have been married since 1964, and we live in a landmark house in Laguna Beach. Our one son never caught the mineral 'bug'. He is instead focusing on work on the fishing fleets out of San Diego and continuing to play drums in a reggae band formed in the seventh grade in Laguna Beach. We maintain a small private collection of minerals with emphasis on native elements, and also collect early California paintings and continue to expand the library. Our library consists of several parts: early works on mineralogy, western exploration, and the California gold rush. We also have the Arizona history collection belonging to the late Richard Bideaux. This library is one of the most extensive in the world and now consists of three rooms at the house.

Early on we both decided that when a day arrived that this business was no 'fun' or interesting, we would leave the scene. Fortunately that day has not materialized and we still enjoy the 'chase' and the friendship of so many wonderful people around the world.

"Seaweed" Gold Harper Brothers Mine. Tuolumne County, California, USA

The 'groupings' in the photos by the VanPelts are always so good, but when you have a specimen like this one - they're even better! This was part of the Charles Crespi collection and most likely found in the 1940s. This one is now at the Natural History Museum of the Smithsonian Institution and on prominent display. The nuggets are from the Ruby Mine in California. 20 cm tall. Harold and Erica VanPelt photograph.

Gold Crystals
Eagle's Nest Mine, Placer County, California, USA

This is an early specimen from the mine and shows beautiful luster and crystallization. The Eagle's Nest Mine is operated by the fourth generation of the family - one man and his two sons make up the entire mine crew. Early on when they employed a shovel operator specimens were 'highgraded' and hit the market under the made up name of "Mystery Wind Mine". This piece is one of our favorites and one of the few pieces we bought for ourselves. 6 x 4 cm. Harold and Erica Van Pelt photograph.

This is one of our classic well-known 'posed' photos by the VanPelts. This assemblage has specimens from Placer County, the leaf gold on the shelf is from Tuolumne County - others from the Eagle's Nest - the nugget is from "California". These photos from the Van-Pelts are so well known that in one case we put an ad in a magazine without ANY identifying information and we still receive phone calls - people said they knew it was ours. One time a well-known mineral magazine tried to imitate the format on their cover and after receiving so many calls about the "Kristalle cover", they gave up on trying it again. By the way, the VanPelts will not do this kind of creativity for anyone else.

by Wayne Leicht and Dona Leicht   154

Gold
Red Ledge Mine, Washington, Nevada County, California, USA

This specimen from the Red Ledge Mine in Nevada County, California is probably one of the most recognized in the world. The very unusual aspect to this specimen is the tree root on the upper right of the specimen. The pocket from which it came was located just a few feet below the surface and had been penetrated by tree roots. The rest of the pocket was filled with dirt and other loose gold specimens. The quartz crystal on the bottom is an added bonus since we rarely see complete well formed quartz crystals with the gold, even 'tho the gold is formed in the quartz veins. This one was also in the Crespi collection and Wayne remembers seeing it on display at the Calaveras County Fair when he was a young boy. It was owned at that time by the Tracy family, who owned the Red Ledge Mine. The daughter, Lyla Tracy, was known to take this specimen to her school class for 'show and tell'. The specimen was found in 1959. We take it on our rounds of 'show and tell'. 14 x 12cm. Harold and Erica VanPelt photograph.

**Cubic Gold Crystals
Australia**

(upper left) This incredibly rare cubic gold specimen was in the Albert Chapman collection and we 'chased' it for over 35 years! In our last visit with Albert a few months before his death, he told us to 'take it all', meaning his entire collection. BUT...sensitive to his attachment to his life's passion we declined and said we would come back another time. After his death, the collection was sent off to the Australian Museum and an Australian collector obtained the balance. In our belief that every specimen eventually winds up where it's supposed to be appreciated the most ... it is now a proud addition to our small collection of golds. 2.5 cm x 2cm.
William McCarty photograph.

**Gold
Eagle's Nest Mine, Placer County, California, USA**

This is a very early specimen from the mine. It was handed down to the current operators from grandfather Garbe who most likely found it in the 1940s. It's just a beautiful thing to look at - we've noticed that the better the crystallization and lustre the less likely the gold will adhere to the specimen. This was a 'floater' with no gold attachment whatsoever. 8 x 4 cm.
Harold and Erica VanPelt photograph.

Gold
Eagle's Nest Mine, Placer County, California, USA

Having said that fine crystallization and brilliance with quartz attachment hardly occurs at the mine, THIS is one of the exceptions. This miniature size specimen is a favorite of all who see it. Our friend, Tana Daugharthy, loved it at first sight and it has been in her collection for 15 years or more. 2.5 x 2 cm. Harold and Erica VanPelt photograph.

Gold Crystals
Eagle's Nest Mine, Placer County, California, USA

This is another one of those 'floaters' from the mine. These are all flattened octahedrons - the quartz seams in the mine are only about 2" thick at best and many of the specimens were squeezed during formation in these small seams. 5 x 3 cm.
Harold and Erica VanPelt photograph.

Gold
Tuolumne County, California, USA

This specimen fascinated the late Dr. Clifford Frondel when he first saw it. It is actually a twin crystal which you can easily see when looking at the back (we should have photographed the back!). That was some 25 years ago and he was our very first houseguest in our new home in Laguna Beach. Over a few fine bottles of wine we spent the day talking minerals and their crystallography. With Frondel you just wanted to listen and learn. Funny how things go over the years - we remained good friends until his death and he was always a source of confirmation on our questions. We ended up with his book collection and reviewing his notes in the margins of many books is an interesting read. 3.5 x 1.5 cm. Harold and Erica VanPelt.

Gold
Eagle's Nest Mine, Placer County, California, USA

This thumbnail specimen was photographed in three different views (front, back, side). It is just one of those interesting octahedrons with hoppered growth and very bright. We sold this to Jim Minette. We have no idea where it might have ended up during the sale of the Minette collection. 1.5 x 1.5cm, Harold and Erica VanPelt photograph.

Gold
Eureka & Grizzly Mine, Tuolumne County, California, USA

This mine was later known as the Harper Brothers Mine and there are few specimens around from this location. Active in recovering specimens back in 1940s, this piece was also part of the Crespi collection. We wish we had a photograph of the back of the specimen as well since it is equally interesting. Very sharp octahedrons and here again no quartz association. Formerly in the Leonard Bedale collection and then to the Minette collection. 3.8 cm. Harold and Erica VanPelt photograph.

**Gold, Alabama Claim of the Crystalline Mine,
Jamestown, Tuolumne County, California, USA**

This was one of the biggest 'strikes' in recent years. The Sonora Mining Company was producing low grade ore and sending it right to the smelter. On Christmas day 1991, the conveyor belt came to a screeching halt - the workers thought a piece of machinery may have come down the belt. Upon close examination no one could believe their eyes - giant, heavy pieces of gold leaf specimens were mucking up the system! This specimen is now in a private collection. 18 x 10 cm. Harold and Erica VanPelt photograph.

Gold
Eagle's Nest Mine, Placer County, California, USA

This is probably our favorite specimen in our collection. This specimen belonged to the Garbe family and was handed down to the current operators of the mine. We can only guess when it was mined - most likely in the 1940s. This was used on street banners in Sacramento and all of the advertising for the sesquicentennial of the California gold rush and the major exhibit which toured around the State. We actually managed to obtain one of those large street banners and it hangs in our shop today. 12 x 8 cm. Harold and Erica VanPelt photograph.

Gold
Eagle's Nest Mine, Placer County, California, USA

This was is just so darn interesting from a crystallographic standpoint. Arborescent and flattened octahedrons and mirror bright. This one dates back to the very early days of our association with the mine and the first appearance in the MR of this and other specimens gave the locality simply as the Michigan Bluff Mining District in Placer County. The owner was so excited about finding a vein that he did not want the exact location given initially. This is currently in a private museum collection in Europe. 8 x 8 cm.
Harold and Erica VanPelt photograph.

Gold
Eagle's Nest Mine, Placer County, California, USA

This one is so photogenic and just pleasing to the eye. 8 x 6 cm.
Harold and Erica VanPelt photograph.

Assorted California gold specimens

Harold and Erica VanPelt photograph.

by Wayne Leicht and Dona Leicht 166

Gold
Alabama Claim, Crystalline Mine
Tuolumne County, California, USA

This is also from the famous "Christmas Pocket" at the mine in Jamestown, California.
Most of the specimens had to be 'unfurled' because they came through the belt and were curled.
Thank nature for the malleability of gold... 8 x 8cm Harold and Erica VanPelt photograph.

The Segerstrom Gold Collection, Tuolumne County, California, USA

The Segerstrom family goes way back in the gold country. Charlie and Marietta Segerstrom (now deceased) lived in Sonora and owned several mines in the area, but we don't think it was the mine were these specimens were found. We don't have a specific location but the general area around Sonora would match other specimens we know about. The Segerstrom family is still in the Sonora area. The collection was on loan to the San Francisco Mint for eons until the family offered it for sale after Marietta's death. Charlie's brother, Henry, is probably the most famous of the family. Henry owned a bunch of bean fields in Orange County near where we live. Those bean fields have turned into one of the most famous shopping centers in the world (South Coast Plaza) and concert halls, theatres, hotels and restaurants - the cultural center of the county. He had little interest in what the Sonora group was doing. Wayne used to spend hours on the porch with Charlie talking about gold mining. Tallest specimen about 30 cm. Harold and Erica VanPelt photograph.

by Wayne Leicht and Dona Leicht   168

Gold
Red Ledge Mine, Washington, Nevada County, California, USA

This specimen came to us from a relative of a dentist who lived in the gold country who had this specimen for over 50 years. An absolutely unique piece from the Red Ledge since we don't see many specimens on matrix from there. We deliberated a long time about selling it, but we did in the end. It was sold to James Horner and is now on display at the Houston Museum of Natural Science. 35 cm tall. Harold nd Erica Van Pelt photograph.

Native gold with unusual 'wire' formations
Magenta Mine, Nevada County, California, USA

"Wire" golds from any locality are extremely rare and an occurrence in California even rarer. We believe that this specimen was found in the 1950s and we obtained it from a collector of gold more than 20 years ago. The Magenta mine is just a portion of the larger complex of the Empire Star mine. We've only seen a few specimens of wire gold from California. 10 x 7 cm. Harold and Erica VanPelt photograph.

Gold
Eagle's Nest Mine, Placer County, California, USA

(left) This is one of the more recent specimens from the mine and is a pleasing spray of crystals on quartz. This is the typical "standard" specimen found in the mine. 6 x 4.5 cm. Robin Hansen photograph.

Chapter Seven: *Specimens from the Scott Rudolph Collection*
by Scott Rudolph

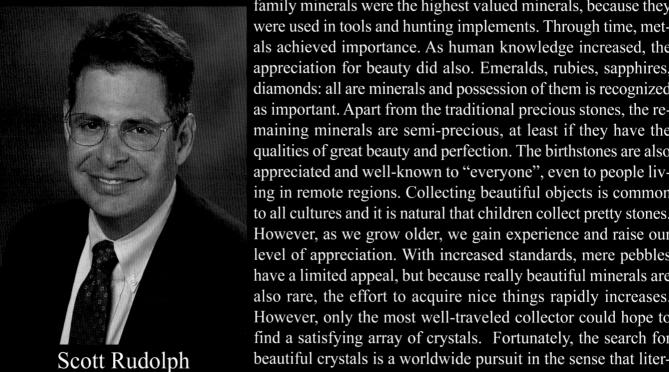

Scott Rudolph

Beautiful gems and minerals are the true treasures. Gold and silver were the original minerals used in coinage and transparent crystals formed the basis of display of wealth. In earliest times, quartz family minerals were the highest valued minerals, because they were used in tools and hunting implements. Through time, metals achieved importance. As human knowledge increased, the appreciation for beauty did also. Emeralds, rubies, sapphires, diamonds: all are minerals and possession of them is recognized as important. Apart from the traditional precious stones, the remaining minerals are semi-precious, at least if they have the qualities of great beauty and perfection. The birthstones are also appreciated and well-known to "everyone", even to people living in remote regions. Collecting beautiful objects is common to all cultures and it is natural that children collect pretty stones. However, as we grow older, we gain experience and raise our level of appreciation. With increased standards, mere pebbles have a limited appeal, but because really beautiful minerals are also rare, the effort to acquire nice things rapidly increases. However, only the most well-traveled collector could hope to find a satisfying array of crystals. Fortunately, the search for beautiful crystals is a worldwide pursuit in the sense that literally millions of people are involved in their recovery. The channels of commerce effectively distribute items of beauty from locations where they are concentrated to places where they are unknown. Crystals of the colorful mineral tourmaline are known in mountainous regions, as are many of the gem crystals and minerals from remote localities pass through a chain from a local miner through marketplaces and traveling buyers eventually, to reach the stage where specimens are presented directly to interested people. The "final" disposition of crystals may occur at conventions and shows, over the internet, by shipped packages, or by direct exchange from other collectors. The collecting and trading or selling of minerals represents an important stage in their conservation. Plants and animals require habitat preservation and the maintenance of the species' populations. Minerals on the other hand are relatively finite and when minerals are exposed on the surface of the Earth, they immediately succumb to weathering – rain, frost, burning desert heat, etc. If crystals are not specifically preserved, they will eventually "perish". My motivation for collecting minerals is their beauty. As Nature's creations, each group of crystals is unique and the specimens, which are picked for my collection are chosen for a variety of reasons. Some specimens have awesome color intensity. Others have a surreal transparency and still others have a rigorous to free-flowing shape, which is appealing. While the marketplace where minerals can be found is large, the "good" specimens are always in short supply. Oftentimes, a lifetime could pass without having an opportunity to acquire a truly great example of a mineral of interest. Sometimes, a bonanza of exquisite crystals may be available. The secret to maximizing opportunity is travel and networking. The marketplace becomes the hunting ground. There is a thrill in knowing about a new discovery and tracking down the source, all the while hoping that a sought after specimen is still in the "wild". The following gallery illustrates a few specimens, which did not "get away" and I am pleased to be able to share with you the pleasure they bring.

Fluorite
Yaogangxian Mine, Hunan Province, China

Pastel colors are much sought after in crystals and fluorite is a species that can be either pastel or brightly colored. Occasionally, fluorite can be a delicate to intense blue resembling glacier ice. The surface of the crystal also has a texture reminiscent of ice and when placed on a matrix of clear quartz and white albite crystals, the scene is complete. 10 x 10.5 x 12 cm. Jeff Scovil photograph.

Schorl Tourmaline with Cleavelandite and Quartz
Skardu, Baltistan, Pakistan

"Basic black and pearls" is a fashion mantra and this specimen emulates those qualities. The big black schorl is bright with attractive striations accentuating the crystal's length. The white "pearls" consist of clusters of bladed white cleavelandite joining the schorl with clear quartz crystals. 9 x 13 x 16 cm. Jeff Scovil photograph.

Aquamarine on Albite
Shengus, Skardu, Baltistan, Pakistan

Aquamarine means the "color of the sea". These spires of aquamarine are closely spaced, but independent of each other. They seem to float on an ocean of frothy white albite showing crystal waves lapping onto the crystal bases. Free-standing gem pocket aquamarine crystals were a great rarity before the Central Asian localities were discovered, but they are still highly prized. 8 x 11.5 x 15 cm. Jeff Scovil photograph.

Manganite
Ilfeld, Harz Mountains, Germany

Manganite is always a black mineral, but it rarely forms outstanding crystals and only an antique discovery represents the finest crystals of its kind. The cluster shows prominent prismatic crystals surrounded by villages of smaller crystals. Each of the manganite crystals shows details suggesting they are formed from the parallel union of rod-like crystals. 4 x 6 x 8 cm. Jeff Scovil photograph.

Fluorite on Quartz and Ferberite
Yaogangxian Mine Yizhang County, Hunan Province, China

Because fluorite is found in so many kinds of deposits, its association with other crystals is as important as the mineral itself. The gorgeous purple crystals have color-banding making them appear like boxes within boxes. The presence of gemmy lightly tinted quartz and black ferberite further give the impression of a remote mountainside with the fluorite on display. 5.5 x 8 x 13 cm. Jeff Scovil photograph.

Scolecite on Stilbite
Nasik Mine, Maharashtra, India

Scolecite was a scarce mineral relegated to only tiny specimens known until the rocks of western India were cut into. In this region, a few localities yielded starbursts of giant scolecite crystals. This radial spray has gemmy rods of scolecite on a pastel salmon pink stilbite crystal which has the vague impression of being a salmon itself. 11 x 14 x 15 cm. Jeff Scovil photograph.

Topaz on Smoky Quartz
Alabashka, Middle Ural Mountains, Russia

Topaz. Sometimes that is all that needs to be said. Several hundred years ago, great discoveries of Topaz were made high in the Ural Mountains. These crystals were immediately
treasured as best of their kind. This gemmy crystal is symmetrical with many small bevels on
the faces while it sets of a smoky quartz crystal contrasting the rigid geometry of the topaz
with a network of white web-like patterns. White cleavelandite blades provide a garnish on
the base. 5 x 8 x 8 cm. Jeff Scovil photograph.

Copper "The Rabbit"
Houghton County, Keweenaw Peninsula, Michigan, USA

Some minerals specimens command attention because they strongly imitate Nature. Although this specimen has been named "The Rabbit", it sometimes makes people think of a Burro. Nonetheless, it is an extraordinary fanciful specimen of crystallized copper from the world's greatest region that yielded native copper. 3 x 10 x 13.5 cm. Jeff Scovil photograph.

Imperial Topaz
Ghundao Hill, Katlang, Mardan District, Pakistan

You have not seen topaz, or any mineral, if you just have one specimen of it. Orange to pinkish orange topaz is widely regarded as the "highest" color topaz may have and these shades have been called "Imperial", because they were fit for jewels owned by emperors. Humble white calcite clings to this extraordinary specimen. 8 x 9 x 9 cm. Jeff Scovil photograph.

Dolomite
Shangbao Pyrite Mine, Hunan, China

Dolomite is usually a mineral discarded by miners, because it generally forms only uninteresting rocks. Crystals that are cloudy white to pink are not particularly rare, but transparent dolomite crystals are very desirable. Only a few dolomites reveal the complexity of their crystal structure such as this nearly transparent specimen where a motif of triangles and hexagons compete with each other. 1.5 x 6 x 6.5 cm. Jeff Scovil photograph.

Pyromorphite
Bunker Hill Mine, Kellogg, Shoshone County, Idaho , USA

Pyromorphite may be a variety of colors even at a single location. Idaho has furnished many examples of this species, but in the 1980s there was a production of many fine groups and clusters, many in extraordinary size and unusual brilliance. One of the color combinations that was much valued was the greenish yellow crystal prism with yellow cap. Typical of pyromorphite from many locations, the flat terminations reveal a corrugated to skeletal texture suggesting that the crystals grew relatively rapidly. 7.5 x 12 x 15 cm. Jeff Scovil photograph.

Inesite
Fengjiashan mine, Daye County, Huangshi Prefecture, Hubei Province, China

By all standards, inesite is very very uncommon. Fine specimens are rare and only a handful of localities come to mind even to seasoned mineral collectors. The most recent important inesite discovery has come from China. They are being found even as this description is being written, but as with all great discoveries, the supply of new specimens will end. While most inesite is bright pink, the Chinese specimens have attained an attractive strawberry tint. 6.6 x 7 x 7.5 cm. Jeff Scovil photograph.

Scorodite
El Cobre Mine, Concepción del Oro, Zacatecas, Mexico

The famous copper mines of Mexico have produced some great examples of blue scorodite. The crystals have the appearance of pyramids with flat tops and some of the faces have varying markings giving heightened interest to their blocky nature. These 2 cm crystals are true giants. 2 x 2.5 x 5.5 cm. Jeff Scovil photograph.

Rubellite Tourmaline with Lepidolite
Jonas Mine, Itatiaia, Minas Gerais, Brazil

Pure rubellite crystals are scarce and deep red ones are more so. The Jonas Mine rubellites rank among the greatest of the rubellites. They are intensely red, bright, and frequently gemmy. This cluster is all the more interesting as it is decorated with sharp crystals of light lilac colored lepidolite mica crystals. 4 x 6 x 9.5 cm. Jeff Scovil photograph.

Emerald
Coscuez Mine, Muzo, Vasquez-Yacopi Mining District,
Boyacá Department, Colombia

Emerald is precious, but all the more so when attached to matrix and when the matrix en-
twines around the crystal, there is a perfect match. 4 x 6.5 x 6.5 cm. Jeff Scovil photograph.

Tanzanite
Merelani Hills Mine, Lelatema Mountains, Arusha, Tanzania

One of the world's newest gems is Tanzanite. Because there is but one location in the world for this gem, it is priced in line with precious gem minerals. This specimen is blessed with a great number of seemingly intersecting lines and closely spaced faces, each canted at a small angle from the next one. The large window into the gem crystal reveals the sapphire sea within. 3 x 7 x 7 cm. Jeff Scovil photograph.

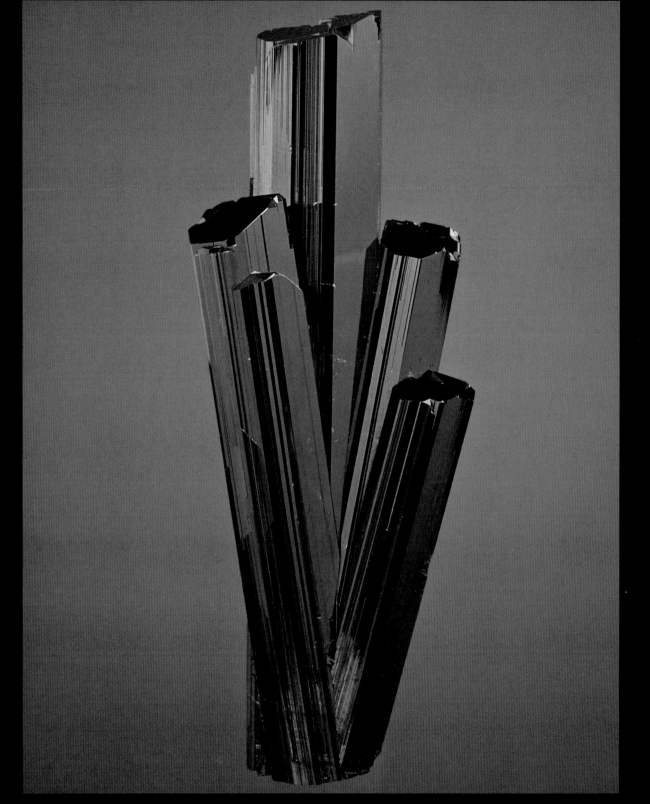

Epidote
Knappenwand, Untersulzbachtal, Salzburg, Austria

Epidote ranks among the 100 common minerals worldwide. As the number of localities increase where large epidote crystals are found, the elegantly smooth faces of these sharply formed crystals remains unmatched aesthetically. 2.5 x 2.7 x 7.5 cm. Jeff Scovil photograph.

Pyromorphite
Daoping Mine, Guilin Prefecture, Guangxi Region, China

Bright yellowish green is a color not frequently seen in large crystals. The large pyromorphite crystals have slight color banding in them as well as having smaller lightly colored sister crystals among the coralline growth of this cluster. 7 x 10 x 10 cm. Jeff Scovil photograph.

Malachite on Shattuckite
Kandesi, Kaokoveld Plateau, Kunene Region, Namibia

Copper minerals may be a variety of colors, but are usually green or blue. It is a real co-incidence when two well-formed copper minerals have such contrasting colors as this one. The light blue crystallized shattuckite is a rarity, but so are well-formed dark green malachite crystals. The shattuckite forms a "clam shell" around the malachite rods. 7 x 8 x 12 cm. Jeff Scovil photograph.

Mimetite
Congreso-Leon Mine, San Pedro Corralitos, Chihuahua, Mexico

Interesting yellow minerals are under-represented in the mineral kingdom and the mimetite from this locality is much appreciated. The heyday of these specimens has passed although occasional new specimens come to light. The yellow "mushrooms" of mimetite glisten and play across the surface of this specimen. 5 x 9 x 13 cm. Jeff Scovil photograph.

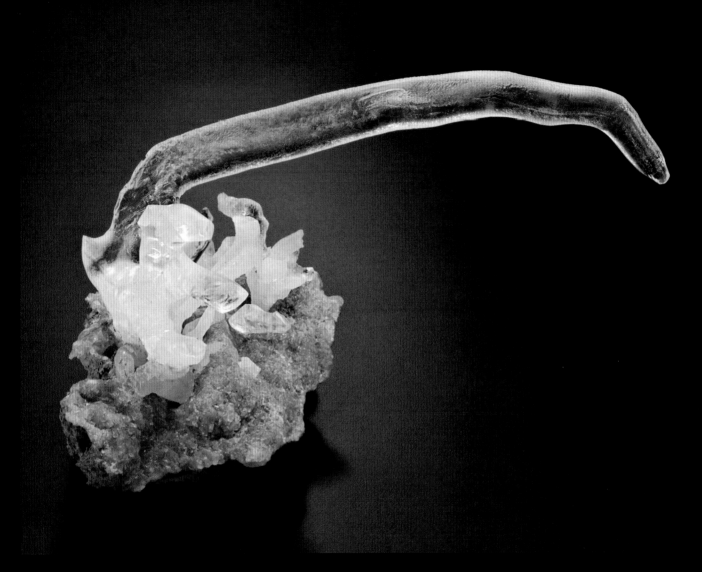

Calcite
Wenshan Mine, Wenshan County, Yunnan Province, China

Calcite forms such a wide variety of shapes, forms, and associations that it is a specialty all by itself. However, this mineral is also known for its surprises. This rounded, bent, and somewhat contorted specimen displays a character rarely seen among the minerals. This "crystal" looks more like a science fiction hero than a mineral specimen. 16 x 17 x 21 cm. Jeff Scovil photograph.

Wulfenite
Red Cloud Mine, La Paz County, Arizona, USA

Wulfenite also has its high-quality standard classic locality and that locality is the Red Cloud Mine. The red wulfenites are rarely matched elsewhere in the world and then the crystals are almost always inferior in size or shape. This particular specimen is rich in well-formed highly complex wulfenite tablets with choice large crystals surrounded by a wealth of perfect crystals of descending size. 6 x 9 x 10 cm. Jeff Scovil photograph.

Pyromorphite
Les Farges Mine, Ussel, Limousin, France

Pyromorphite means "formed by fire" although in this specimen it could as easily mean "formed as though it were fire". The pattern of crystals mimics green flames superimposed on wildly varying positions. 4 x 4.5 x 6 cm. Jeff Scovil photograph.

Calcite with Dioptase Inclusions
Tsumeb, Namibia

Quiet elegance and simplicity have their place among the qualities in a crystallized specimen. This nearly perfect rhombohedron, a "distant relative of the cube", is shown looking
down the principle axis of the crystal showing three-fold symmetry. The blue-green dioptase
crystals included near the base seem to lift the specimen off its matrix. 2 x 3 x 4 cm. Jeff Scovil
photograph.

Cerussite
Tsumeb, Namibia

Tsumeb is often rated as the world's best mineral locality, because so many of its minerals rank among the world's best of species. While many of the Tsumeb minerals are brightly colored, none can best the intriguing twin growth of cerussite. This lead mineral is known for its complex twins and even its reticulated growth, but Tsumeb's cerussite reticulations are so remarkable that people who never have seen a museum mineral specimen before marvel at the intricacy of this mineral's patterns. 2.5 x 5 x 10 cm. Jeff Scovil photograph.

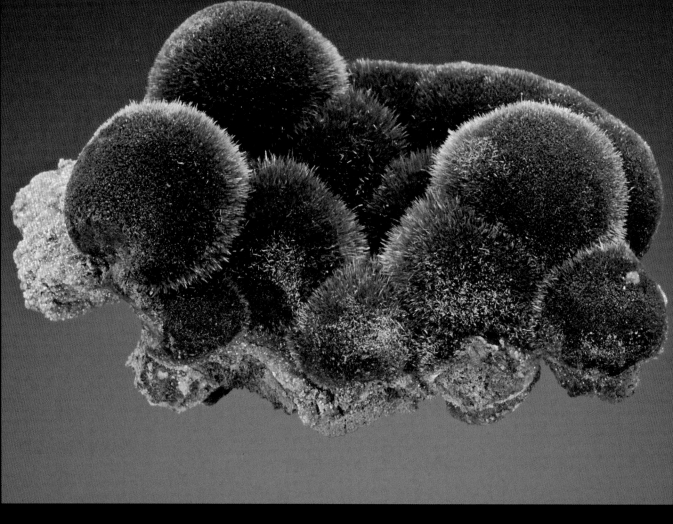

Malachite
Tsumeb, Namibia

Malachite is one of the important ores of copper and it appears in many forms. Tsumeb is noted for its needle crystals and on rare occasions the mine yielded "pincushions" of clusters, but as malachite is also brittle, perfect specimens were a rarity. This robust cluster shows malachite pincushions at varying levels with some clusters having equal length crystals and some clusters showing needles of slightly varying lengths. 3.5 x 4 x 6.5 cm. Jeff Scovil photograph.

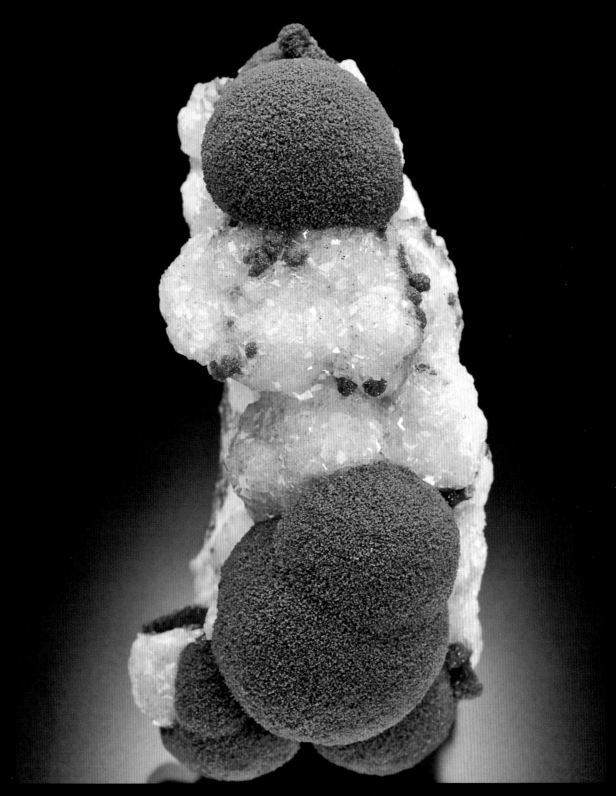

Rosasite on Dolomite
Tsumeb, Namibia

Rosasite is a chemically distant relative to malachite, but in this case it only slightly resembles its cousin as it has a blue cast. The botryoidal shapes of the coalescing rosasite against the white calcite with green accents are remarkable examples of a mineral that usually forms in miniature elsewhere in the world. 3.5 x 4 x 7 cm. Jeff Scovil photograph.

by Scott Rudolph   198

Mimetite with Bayldonite
Tsumeb, Namibia

Mimetite ideally forms hexagonal prisms, but rarely does it have a well-defined shape.
Botryoids and rounded crystals are more common. Again, Tsumeb has some of the high-stan-
dard examples in the world. These yellow crystals are lightly color frosted on their exterior
and are set in a bright green field of the rare mineral bayldonite. 5 x 6 x 7.5 cm. Jeff Scovil
photograph.

Elbaite
Pederneira mine, Sao Jose de Safira, Minas Gerais, Brazil

This is a wondeful 'crossed swords" tourmaline. The crystals display the full spectrum known to tourmaline. 19.6 cm high. Jeff Scovil photograph.

Pentagonite
Wagholi Quarry, Pune District, Maharashtra, India

Pentagonite is a unique mineral. It gets its name from having what look like five-sided crystals, a shape forbidden by Nature, as that pattern doesn't fill space completely. Its chemical composition includes vanadium, an element, which seldom makes a blue color. This one specimen from western India probably contains as much pentagonite as has been found, combined, from all of the other countries in the world. 3 x 3.5 x 3.5 cm. Jeff Scovil photograph.

Wulfenite on Descloizite
Ahumada Mine, Sierra de Los Lamentos, Chihuahua, Mexico

Wulfenite is another mineral, which offers beautiful variety in its coloration and crystal shapes. These crystals from the "Mountain of Lament" are so characteristic as to be immediately recognized by connoisseurs of the mineral. The square tablets have a Salvador Dali quality

Indicolite Tourmaline and Quartz
Benedito Mine, Água Boa, Minas Gerais, Brazil

It is a pleasure to find two good-looking minerals together on a specimen. The indicolite tourmaline is a beauty and it is attached to a beautiful quartz crystal. The quartz has frosted white stair-steps leading up to an etched apex of the crystal and the upward movement is taken over by the shaft of the gemmy blue indicolite which also has an etched apex. 4.5 x 5 x 12 cm. Jeff Scovil photograph.

Rhodochrosite on Tetrahedrite
Graham's Pocket, Sweet Home Mine, Alma, Park County, Colorado, USA

Red minerals have the most popular color for mineral collectors' tastes and you'd expect that a mineral named "red color", rhodochrosite, would not disappoint you. Most rhodochrosite is pink, however, and truly red examples are much sought after. The Sweet Home Mine ranks head and shoulders above all other occurrences for large, choice, and vibrant red crystals. The counter-balancing deep crimson rhodochrosite crystals on this specimen are relentlessly cap-tivating and never lose their appeal. 7 x 13 x 10 cm. Jeff Scovil photograph.

Chapter Eight: *Polychrom Minerals*
by Laurent Thomas

By my eighth birthday, I was already "crazy" about minerals. I will be forever indebted to my parents for recognizing and supporting my mineral hobby by joining the local mineralogical club and actively participating in the field trips sponsored by the club. Month after month, year after year they accompanied me to the fields and mines of the classic mineral localities in France.

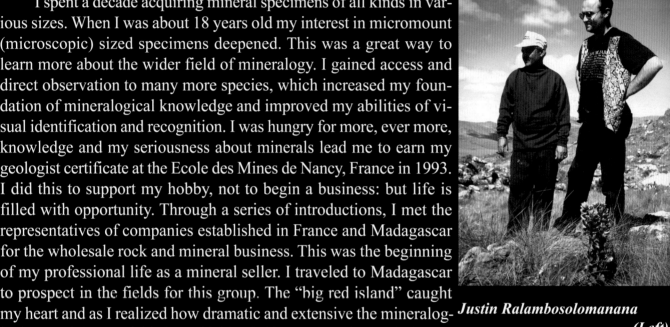

I spent a decade acquiring mineral specimens of all kinds in various sizes. When I was about 18 years old my interest in micromount (microscopic) sized specimens deepened. This was a great way to learn more about the wider field of mineralogy. I gained access and direct observation to many more species, which increased my foundation of mineralogical knowledge and improved my abilities of visual identification and recognition. I was hungry for more, ever more, knowledge and my seriousness about minerals lead me to earn my geologist certificate at the Ecole des Mines de Nancy, France in 1993. I did this to support my hobby, not to begin a business: but life is filled with opportunity. Through a series of introductions, I met the representatives of companies established in France and Madagascar for the wholesale rock and mineral business. This was the beginning of my professional life as a mineral seller. I traveled to Madagascar to prospect in the fields for this group. The "big red island" caught my heart and as I realized how dramatic and extensive the mineralogical potential was of this beautiful land, I knew that I had to build my own business and search for minerals and explore in my own way. I

Justin Ralambosolomanana (Left)
Laurent Thomas (Right)

wanted to explore the underground treasures of Madagascar. A friend who is a respected geologist and I begin two local companies in order to explore the underground treasures of Madagascar. In this business, we mine, promote, buy and sell the minerals of Madagascar; we are totally immersed in this business every single day. We had immediate success as significant and popular minerals were discovered including big amethyst scepter quartz, green fuchsite phantom quartz, amethyst scepters with Japan-law twins, new yellow "rhodizites" that were later named londonite. The work has been rewarding and fun. I also met Justin Ralambosolomanana in Madagascar who became my spiritual father. His spirt still ties me to Madagascar.

In 2001, our well-organized team working in Madagascar decided to focus on a stronger sales model and I went back to France to build *Polychrom Minerals*. We began participating in international gem fairs; including Tucson, Munich and the Sainte-Marie-Aux-Mines shows.

More significant minerals were discovered at our mines including blue spinel in dodecahedron shaped crystals, hot pink beryl that soon was described as the new mineral pezzottaite, gemmy multiple twins of yellow calcite, epitactic growth of hematite on rutile, and recently green liddicoatite crystals of exceptional quality. Just prior to the release of this book, incredible flashy yellow-green chrysoberyl crystals on matrix, in association with pale scheelite and taaffeite specimens were uncovered.

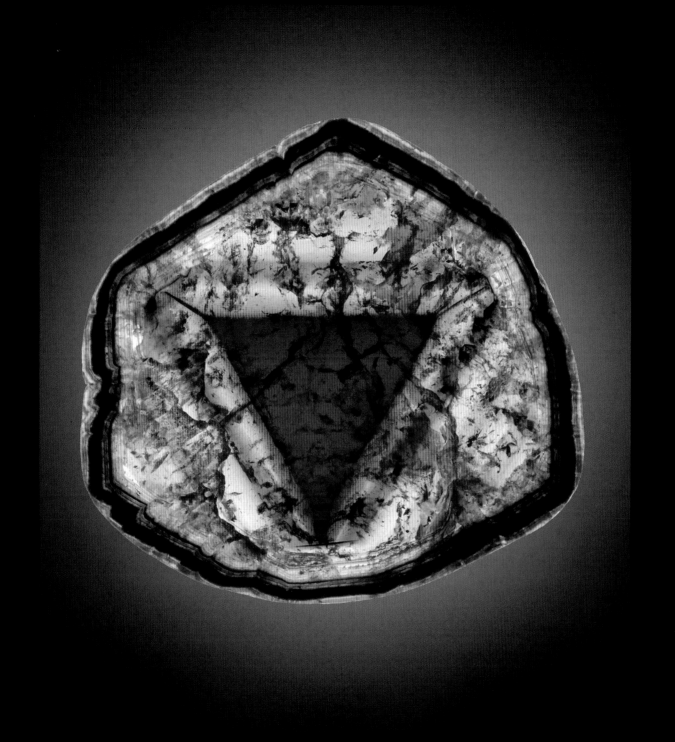

Liddicoatite/Elbaite
"The rice fields", Alakamisy-Inteny, Fianarantsoa Province, Madagascar.

This tourmaline slice is very aesthetic regarding the combination of a truly deep red tri-angular zone surrounded by blue and pink chevrons and set up nicely by the dark outside dark green and yellow green rings which create a frame. This 4.2 cm specimen is a great classic. Jeff Scovil photograph crystallization process, followed by corrosion and dissolution of the earlier formed crystal. The process destroyed a part of the green matter between the "star" branches and then a third phase with hues of pink to orange overgrew the original corroded crystal. This Nature's creation really looks like a stained glass church window. The size of the crystal is amazing too, and came from a gigantic tourmaline boulder found in an alluvial deposit. This is one of the occurrences in a rice field. The specimen is 23 cm wide. Laurent Thomas photograph

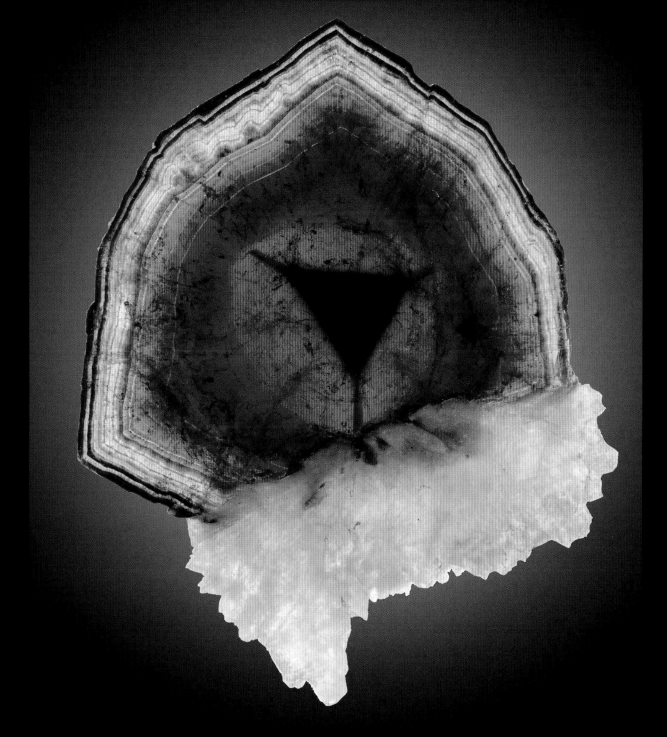

Liddicoatite/Elbaite
Tsitondroina, Ihosy, Fianarantsoa Province, Madagascar.

This is a very aesthetic specimen showing a very strong pink center ring that hosts a black triangle with dark red star branches, all surrounded with tens of very thin layers of colors from pale pink to yellow and green. The outside ring is dark brown, and gently creates a frame. The albite that is attached to the crystal is part of the slice, which is very unusual and nice. The original crystal was fresh, found from a pocket in a hard pegmatite. The specimen is 9.6 cm tall. Jeff Scovil photograph

Liddicoatite/Elbaite
Vohitrakanga, Antsirabe, Antananarivo Province, Madagascar.

This specimen has very rare purple colors, set up in a wonderful interlayered pattern of triangles and chevrons. The combination with the hues of green and the black external ring creates a truly amazing piece. This is one of my favorite tourmaline slices of all that I have en-countered. The specimen is 6.8 cm wide. Marc Lefèvre photograph

Hematite on Rutile
Tetikana, Ambatofinandrahana, Fianarantsoa Province, Madagascar.

Epitactic growth of hematite on rutile is well-known and is even considered to be a classic case in mineralogy. However, this combination in the "reverse" order of growth is extremely rare and was practically never known before this amazing discovery, except in micro-sized crystals. The deposit, in high temperature and pressure origin rocks, yielded very few specimens, most of which were small and imperfect. We tried to dig further, but we had to stop our investigations after some meters when the mineralized vein had totally disappeared, with absolutely no hint left of finding other lens. This specimen is 4.9 cm tall. Louis-Dominique Bayle photograph.

by Laurent Thomas 210

Calcite - Twinned Two Ways
Sambava, Antsiranana Province, Madagascar

The best of the twinned calcites first found in Madagascar in 2001 and then again in 2004 are made up with two-way twinned crystals: yellow, sharp, and gemmy. The architecture of the best groups recovered during the mining operations is very aesthetic. This piece is one of my favorites. The underlayer of microcrystalline quartz creates a small matrix base for the multiple twins. These twins are very clear and have an excellent golden yellow color. The luster is incredibly bright. The specimen is 8.4 cm wide. Louis-Dominique Bayle photograph.

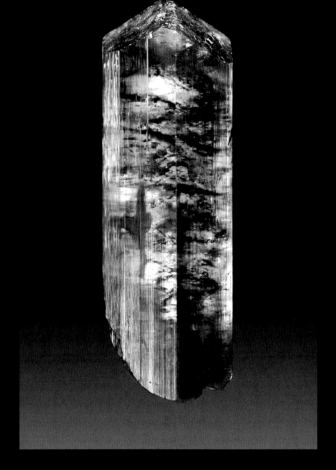

Blue-Cap on Green Tourmaline
Ambatoroka, Ambatondrazaka, Toamasina Province, Madagascar

This specimen comes from a very unusual locality that gave a very small one-time discovery. We never could find another crystal showing this combination of colors. We searched diligently for another, but we did stop the investigations after having spent more money than planned on the project. The specimen is 6.2 cm tall. Louis-Dominique Bayle photograph.

Green Tourmaline
Bevaondrano, Ikalamavony, Fianarantsoa Province, Madagascar

This crystal is the nicest we found in one of our more recent mining projects. In this mine pockets are always very small, but the quality of the tourmaline is great. This tourmaline is a truly giant bright green crystal, made of the best gemmy quality. The architecture of this specimen is fantastic and showing divergence of the prism and very nice terminations rich in facets. The spray of crystals is half very gemmy and half almost white and opaque, with just a very thin pale pink layer at the interface of the two parts: both unusual and delicate. This crystal is naturally healed at the bottom. 13.7 cm tall. Louis-Dominique Bayle photograph.

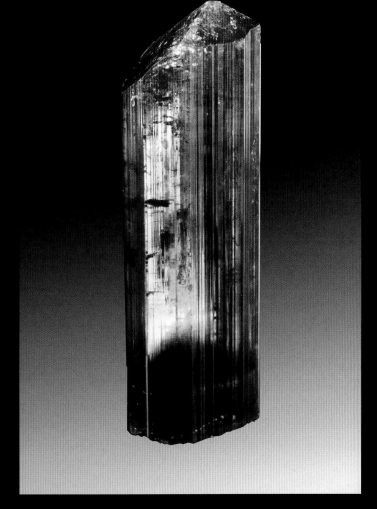

Red-Cap Polychrome Liddicoatite
Anjanabonoina, Betafo, Fianarantsoa Province, Madagascar

Liddicoatite tourmaline is very rare considering the number of pegmatites actually mined in the world, and especially if compared to the amount of elbaite that is produced. In Madagascar, liddicoatite occurs in a wide variety of shapes and colors and is absolutely fantastic in quality. The crystal-producing pockets are not frequent, but we are tracking them with great care. This specimen is 7.4 cm tall, Louis-Dominique Bayle photograph.

As dealers, we focus on acquiring and selling the very finest, most beautiful, and most perfect of all mineral specimens. We assess each piece within the context of other known examples and explain to clients why any particular example is among the very best. We have spent the past 25 years studying and refining our acquisition criteria while presenting mineral specimens within the realm and context of fine art.

Mineral specimens are not like collecting stamps, coins, or baseball cards – those are basically judged on demand, rarity, and condition. Unlike other collectibles, minerals are closer to fine art, each mineral is unique and must be individually judged. These criteria can often be subjective (as in; "the eye of the beholder") or more concrete. We have designed this point system to help collectors more accurately assess how a given specimen ranks among its peers and how it compares to the finest known. These provide some reference points while leaving open the possibility that a specimen can be beautiful and important simply because you enjoy its appearance or that it impacts your senses.

It has always been our personal habit to rank specimens on a 1-10 scale. *Stuart and Donna Wilensky*
We recommend to all collectors to strive to own "10s". There are always specimens that are so vastly superior, so amazingly wondrous, of such shocking beauty and quality, that they must rate above all others; those are the nearly unobtainable Holy Grails I affectionately call – The "11s." An "11" is truly the finest known example of any species, and, you will know one when you see it – we assure you. Below are the factors we consider with an example of each.

1. Aesthetics: This includes the overall appearance or beauty of the specimen. Aesthetic appreciation will vary from "eye to eye", but some basic parameters are universal: crystal isolation and/or well defined individual crystals, crystallized matrix, contrasting colors and textures, crystals of differing size and height, three dimensional viewing angles, specimens which (to quote our friend and master collector, Steve Smale) have "good horizons", or in other words, interesting and well developed top edges where your eye is drawn initially. Just as any work of art it must have pleasing aesthetic arrangement to your eye. This is simply a visual reference to the appeal of the mineral as one would look at any sculpture. The intrinsic value of aesthetic minerals is the pleasure you get from viewing them. Very Subjective.

2. Balance: Related to aesthetics. How do crystals and matrix relate to each other in size, ratio, and form? How do they interact with space? Consider angles, length, thickness, and arrangement. Crystals should look proportional to each other, juxtaposed in interesting and eye appealing ways, or harmoniously on matrix and counter-balanced. Subjective.

Fluorite on Muscovite
Hunza River Valley, Northern Areas, Pakistan

Aesthetics and Balance. The counter-diagonals on this specimen (10 cm wide) are exciting. The major crystal edges of the pink fluorite are compelling, while the subordinate blades of the muscovite mica increase the overall visual energy of the specimen.

3. Crystal Quality, Form, and Definition: This assesses crystal sharpness, termination, and form. For this judgment, crystal faces should form without interruption; angles and planes should intersect with clean definable lines. Take into account the sharpness of edges (depending upon the species). Ask yourself if the terminations are symmetrical, proportionate, well defined, and attractively shaped. The sides and faces of each crystal should be well developed. Terminations that are complex are usually more desirable, they should attract your eye, and not distract. Somewhat Subjective

4. Color: Saturation: "Vivid, bright, intense, colorful"; these are all considered positive qualities for most species. How does the specimen compare in color to other known examples? Normally deeper more saturated color is desirable. Minerals, which are transparent, can actually be less valuable if too dark and light does not transmit through the crystal. These criteria are somewhat subjective, primarily due to the type of lighting when viewing the mineral. You will see differences in color when viewing specimens in daylight or artificial light: incandescent, halogen or fluorescent. Color perception is directly related to lighting, but still measurable in relation to other known examples under the same lighting conditions. Somewhat Subjective

5. Contrast: How do the crystals and matrix contrast with each other in color and texture? This is fairly straightforward in definition. Examples: Dark on light, clear on opaque, smooth on coarse, etc. Contrast delineates crystal edges, sets boundaries and outlines, and creates a visual perception which is more three-dimensional and thus more eye appealing. Not Subjective

6. Luster: Analyze the surface of every crystal and see how it interacts with light and reflection. There are many descriptive terms for luster: glassy, resinous, reflective, metallic, wet, shiny, etc. Radiance, or reflected light, is highly appealing to the eye, like the gleam of Gold, a glint of light, or the shimmer of water. While these are all very good for descriptions, I am more interested in a specimen if the luster catches my eye, my attention, and makes a specimen more appealing. Dull luster is always negative on main crystals, but in some instances on a matrix it can enhance contrast. Somewhat Subjective

Aquamarine and Schorl
Shigar, Baltistan, Pakistan

Crystal Quality and Luster. Three different minerals display their geometrical qualities on this 7 cm tall specimen. The dominant aquamarine (10 cm tall) shows its six-sided prism with complementary forms on the termination while the schorl tourmaline shows its three-sided crystal shape with complementary forms on top both resting on white cleavelandite blades. Each mineral conforms to the strict expectations of perfect crystal growth.

7. Transparency: This obviously only applies to those species which are usually transparent and takes into account the varying degrees of transparency from "pure water clear" to opaque, within the context of what is known about the specific species. Any species not commonly found in transparent crystals is far more valuable when they are. The commonly used term; "Gem" or "Gemmy" implies the piece has a gem like appearance. That is the highest form of transparency and is sought after in all species. The property of a solid object being transparent has for millennia intrigued and fascinated humans. We are drawn to objects that are bright. The light shining through a crystal should create a luminescent glow. Not Subjective.

8. Perfection: This relates to the physical condition, lack of damage, or appearance of damage. We often say, "if it looks like damage, then it is damage". There are different categories of damage. The smallest unit of damage has been called the "Wilber" (named for one of America's greatest mineral collectors, and our good friend, Dave Wilber – not because his minerals had "Wilbers", but, because they did not). Dings, nicks, breaks, or cleaves, on a crystal are part of the reality of collecting minerals. Very few are truly perfect. Damage that is noticeable and interrupts the beauty of a specimen is not acceptable. Often a crystal will have what is known as a "contact". Contacts are where a crystal was up against or grew next to another crystal or matrix. This is natural and as long as they are not unsightly, they are acceptable. Included in these criteria are repairs and restorations, as well. We are of the opinion that repair and restoration is acceptable both when it is invisible, or nearly invisible, does not impact the beauty or aesthetics, and/or when the specimen is considered the finest, or among the finest, known examples. This must be considered when assessing specimens that are considered so magnificent, rare, and important, that repair/restoration is unavoidable to preserve a specimen. Not Subjective.

Tanzanite
Merelani Hills, Tanzania

Color, Contrast, Luster, Perfection: The color of a mineral evokes our preferences immediately. Many regard red to be the ultimate color, while blues, greens, oranges or even colorless or black may be a favorite "color". Within a mineral there needs to be contrast to display the various qualities a crystal may have, while the luster by itself draws one to a specimen. Each criterion works on our consciousness. This tanzanite (6.4 x 3.2 cm) obviously has strong color and it shows variety in intensity with dark areas contrasting with lighter zones. The image has subtle light reflections promising the brightness the crystal has in our hands. Perfection is a quality that is somewhat learned and somewhat visceral. Collectors familiarize themselves with specimens of particular species and remember details of what they have seen, even striving to remember the history of specimens, including a series of prestigious former owners. Regarding perfection, however, the concept of an ideal crystal emerges for each individual. If the collector has also studied crystallography, the appreciation may range from artistic unconformity to rigid principles of geometry, but crystals that are blemish-free command the most respect.

be classed as the largest gem crystal of a species yet found. This can be significant and in the mineral kingdom large perfect crystals are valued due to rarity in relation to any smaller examples. A large crystal in and of itself is not significant. This criterion is only for large crystals that are equal or superior to smaller examples of the same mineral. For example: An Aquamarine crystal that is 2 cm tall, gem clear, top color and on a beautiful matrix, is less important then one of exactly the same quality that is 8 cm tall. Five centimeter tall fabulous Aqua's are not uncommon, twenty cm tall examples are far less common. This criterion becomes more important in species that are rarely found in large sizes. We limit this factor to "Somewhat Important" due to the fact that not all collectors want larger specimens. Not Subjective

10. Wow Factor! Yes, the "Wow Factor", perhaps the most important of all criteria, and the least scientific. This one is both visual and visceral – the indefinable essence of any work of art, how it affects you and moves you emotionally and artistically. Here is how one judges the "Wow Factor"; When you open the box, or walk into a room, and see the specimen for the very first time in person and you utter the word – "WOW!" That's it. Basically you are saying everything you need to know about the specimen. If it passes the "Wow" test then you begin applying the other 9 criteria stated above.

Aquamarine
Fiker-Nagar Mine, Northern Areas, Pakistan

Crystal Size and Wow factor: Big crystals always have more attention gathering power then tiny crystals almost to the exclusion of other considerations. The Wow Factor satisfies our criteria when we look at a specimen and we are immediately impressed. This aquamarine specimen (10 cm wide) has multiple large crystals, perfection, aesthetic qualities, etc., which immediately give it a high Wow index.

The Wow factor is Very Important, Very Subjective, and, of course, Very Personal.

The following gallery illustrates some of our criteria of mineral specimens possessing artistic qualities. Some of the specimens show a variety of our criteria very well, but there may be only several factors in a particular specimen, which satisfy a collector's appreciation and expectations of what qualities a species "should" have.

Amethyst on Quartz
Jackson Crossroads, Wilkes County, Georgia, USA

Amethyst has certain peculiarities. It almost always has a gradation in color. It is also un-commonly found in doubly terminated crystals. The crystals are frequently asymmetrical, and tamethyst is not commonly found on contrasting matrix. This 7 cm tall amethyst and quartz specimen from Jackson Crossroads is beautiful for many reasons outlined in our criteria and its aesthetics appeal to us. The solitary crystal dominates the specimen. Color is intense and contrasts with a white field of quartz while perfection and aesthetic appeal are high, and most of all, these factors are balanced.

Purple Fluorapatite
Pulsifer Quarry, Mount Apatite, Auburn, Androscoggin County, Maine, USA

   Apatite has been called "Queen of the Phosphates" as it is one of the showiest minerals in the entire mineral class that is based on phosphate. This doubly terminated 3.3 cm long crystal on 21 x 16.3 cm matrix was found in 1967 by Skip Szenics and this specimen remains the world's best of its kind. A subordinate, but more famous crystal from this locality. the "Roebling Apatite", was owned by Washington Roebling and originally offered to him at the astonishingly high price of $500 (possibly a record high price for a non-gem mineral in the time period - 1913). When this apatite crystal locality was discovered in 1900, it immediately set the standard for beauty in the species and the standard has not been surrendered to another location. Interestingly, the pink bed of cookeite the crystal rests on is probably one of the best of its species, as well. The back side of the specimen is noteworthy as it contains gem cinnamon brown tourmaline. The "discovery moment" for this crystal is illustrated in Peter Bancroft's 1984 book, "*Gem & Crystal Treasures*".

Topaz and Quartz

Ghundao Hill, Katlang, Mardan District, Northern Areas, Pakistan

Delicate rose pink topaz crystal in the center of a 6.4 x 6.4 cm plate with a well-formed quartz crystal. The color is rare and the crystal is transparent. Combined with its high luster, balance, contrast, and other factors, this is a very fine specimen.

Kunzite
Córrego do Urucum Pegmatite, Minas Gerais, Brazil

Kunzite is among the most sought after of purple gem crystals. It can have remarkable color intensity, which can vary in shade depending if viewed on the termination or through different sides of the crystal. This gem crystal (21 x 16 x 7.5 cm) shows contrast dramatically, a property much desired in a single crystal that has no additional minerals to provide context or contrast.

Rubellite with Cleavelandite and Lepidolite
Kamgal, Kunar Province, Afghanistan

This is an outstanding Rubellite crystal (20 x 30 cm). It has a flared habit due to s
vergent overgrowth of secondary crystals on pink lepidolite studded white cleavelan

Topaz
Virgem da Lapa, Minas Gerais, Brazil

Topaz crystal (12.5 cm tall) showing exciting blue coloration with white cleavelandite blades and blocky microcline with deep mauve lepidolite.

Topaz with Smoky Quartz and Cleavelandite
Dassu, Baltistan, Pakistan

This is a wonderful combination specimen of two well-crystallized minerals on an attractive matrix (12.5 cm wide). The peach to sherry-colored topaz is complimented by light brown smoky quartz crystals on white cleavelandite blades and blocky microcline. This specimen shows a sequence of formation building on the base microcline with succeeding growth by cleavelandite, quartz, and topaz.

Morganite with Kunzite on Cleavelandite
Paprok, Nuristan Province, Afghanistan

When two world-class species are present on a specimen. it immediately has achieved greatness. This Morganite and Kunzite has the Aesthetics and Wow Factors to place it among the world's greatest specimens of any kind. The color intensity is high along with the complimentary character of purple versus pink set on white cleavelandite and gray quartz matrix. The 20 x 20 cm size is almost ideal and this specimen qualifies as an example for an "11".

A personal biography should include the life-defining moments. We are a product of our past. Many people's lives have a small incident, a treasured memory, or a chance encounter which shaped whom they would become. Mineral collecting and photography are my personal passions and as with many of life's passions, they began when we were impressionable. I began collecting at the age of 4 years old just after seeing the imaginative and visually stimulating Walt Disney film "Fantasia". The charm and character of the images were magical. The scenes with dinosaurs immediately influenced me and just four days later, my mother gave me a fossil trilobite and a mineral – a classic agate. This was my defining moment and I started to collect fossil and minerals. After some years, I stopped collecting fossils as they did not continue to excite me as they formerly had. However, I was a collector and so started a new collection, this time of meteorites and in 12 years the collection grew to over 700 specimens from all over world. The mineral collection continues to grow, as well, and for the moment has over 1200 specimens ranging in size from "micro" to "cabinet size". The majority of my specimens come

Matteo Chinellato

from Italy, but the scope of the localities ranges worldwide. One sub-collection contains nearly a thousand specimens of micromounts whose beauty may only be appreciated through the microscope. A new passion emerged from a old passion, the photography of minerals. It was always one of my dreams to take images of the micro minerals that I observed under the microscope. Unfortunately, photography through the microscope usually does no justice to the mineral world in miniature. Most images look flat and lifeless. With this idea, I started building a collection of photographic equipment especially adapted for taking photos without using a microscope. One challenge I have taken as a priority is to accurately show the luster of a crystal. The technical aspects of sharpness, depth of field, etc. must also be at their best, but luster is a subtle quality sometimes poorly captured in photographs.

After 15 years as an amateur photographer, I progressed to becoming a professional photographer: thus making a hobby into work. Many of my mineral photos are used in mineralogical books, reviews, mineral exhibition posters, brochures, catalogs, etc. Within the small community of mineral enthusiasts, scientists, and mineral professionals, I am also fortunate to have access to many museum collections and am permitted to take photos of what I want and the same is true for many important private collections. The gallery here shows specimens both from my own collection as well as from museum and private collections. You may see some more photos in my Mindat gallery at http://www.Mindat.org/user-5018.html#2_0_0_0_0_

Elbaite
Grotta d'Oggi Quarry, San Piero in Campo,
Elba Island, Livorno Province, Tuscany, Italy

Elbaite crystals from the original locality on Elba Island are very distinctive and are particularly noted for color bands that are seemingly layered throughout the length of the crystal. The purple and lilac colors are very much sought after. This specimen (5.7 x 2.7 cm) shows spires of polychrome elbaite with quartz and albite.

Right: Detail from the above specimen showing a 5.76 mm elbaite crystal with lovely lilac color zone.

Grossular (Garnet Group)
Bellecombe, Châtillon, Aosta Valley, Italy

Garnets are a group of very symmetrical minerals, which can display a beautiful range of colors. Grossular is known for its gemmy red character, although it may be green or even colorless. Some garnets such as almandine or pyrope are almost always deep red to rose red. This 3.3 mm crystal shows some asymmetry and small "extra" faces typical of garnets. Pale green platy crystals of clinochlore form a nest for the grossular. Domenico Preite Collection.

Left: Rose red almandine garnet on muscovite. (3.3 mm) I Mondei, Montescheno, Antrona Valley, Piedmont, Italy,

Domenico Preite Collection.

Andradite variety Demantoid
Sferlun Asbestos mine, Malenco Valley,
Sondrio Province, Lombardy, Italy

Remarkable nearly emerald green de-mantoid garnet crystal nestled in creamy white fibrous matrix. (above) Although only 2 mm in size, close-up photography can bring this crystal jewel to radiant glory. Collection of Domenico Preite.

Right: Perfect 9.42 x 9.1 mm single crystal with a "ghost" inclusion repeated by the light refraction of the crystal faces. Collection of the Natural History Museum of Milan.

Monazite-(Ce)
Trimouns Talc Mine, Luzenac, Ariège, Midi-Pyrénées, France

Golden yellow monazite-(Ce) crystals on dolomite. Field of view is 5.5 millimeters wide. While monazite-(Ce) is an ore for rare-earth elements used for a wide variety of technological products ranging from strong magnets to polishing compounds. Its usual crystals are opaque reddish brown to dark brown and frequently found in chucky pieces or sand grains. Occasionally, monazite-(Ce) attains great beauty and because of the rarity of beautiful monazite-(Ce) crystals, they are always treasured when found.

Mimetite
Rouez mine, Sarthe,
Pays de Loire, France

Starburst clusters of nearly colorless mimetite crystals with bluish green malachite. Both fields of view less than 2 millimeters wide. Often, when minerals are being found, the collector notes the presence of minute crystals on a rock and only discovers their full beauty on closer examination when at home.

Hematite
Monte Somma, Naples Province, Campania, Italy

Iron minerals such as hematite are the ores from which iron and steel are made. This 1 cm cluster from the Mount Vesuvius region forms an elegant iridescent "cathedral" grouping of crystals.

Magnetite
Formazza Valley, Piedmont, Italy

Magnetite is also a common iron ore mineral, but it also is present within humans and even helps migratory birds know in which direction they are flying. This crystal is only 5.4 millimeters tall, but shows many pleasing characteristics. The strength of its elegantly ideal form is compelling, but it also has a surface iridescence, which is attractive, although if it were uniformly black, the presentation would still make this a good specimen representing its kind.

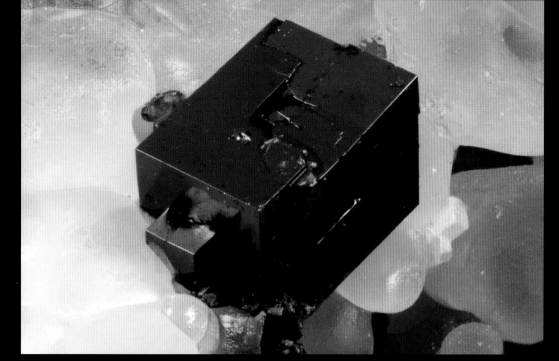

Perovskite
San Vito Quarry, Monte Somma, Naples Province, Campania, Italy

Monte Somma and its twin volcano, Mount Vesuvius, are famous for the variety of exquisite minerals in them. This 2.2 mm crystal shows typical blocky habit with interesting offsets and intergrowths. The black color is due to enrichment of trace elements.
Collection of the Natural History Museum of Milan.

Perovskite
Rocca Sella, Piedmont, Italy

Dark amber-colored 4.3 mm perovskite crystals in quartz. These crystals have a gemmy appearance as they are relatively pure. Domenico Preite collection.

Sphalerite
Lengenbach Quarry, Binn Valley, Wallis, Switzerland

Sphalerite is a chameleon mineral. The Latin root of its name means "to deceive', because of its wide variety of appearances. With increasing substitution by various elements for the mineral's essential Zinc, the color may be yellow, brown, orange, red, or green. It is usually opaque black or brown black, but when pure it is transparent and colorless. Sphalerite is also an "uncooperative" mineral and its crystals are rarely symmetrical and are uncommonly isolated. This sphalerite crystal is just under 2 mm, but is still one of the species' champions. Crystals of sphalerite are ideally a tetrahedron and this crystal shows a dominant equilateral triangular face towards the viewer, but the apices of the triangle are cut by a second, smaller tetrahedron at a right angle to the larger one. Additionally, this sphalerite has more faces, which cut into the edges of the dominant tetrahedron. These faces cutting the tetrahedron's edges are tristetrahedral in form. However, despite the complexity of the faces present, this crystal still has ideal proportions. Domenico Preite collection.

Humite
Monte Somma, Naples Province, Campania, Italy

Humite is a not too distant relative of olivine and, just like its cousin, it rarely forms beautiful crystals. The Monte Somma volcano has yielded some of the best humite crystals known. This delicate yellow humite is just under 2 mm in size, yet it is gorgeous. It is "reclined" on the matrix rather than presenting itself erect in the classical orientation found in textbooks. The termination and prismatic faces show a subtle set of alternating light and dark bands where closely spaced faces reflect light. Careful examination of the image shows this crystal to be rich in a variety of smooth faces.

Haüyne
Mendig, Eifel Mountains, Rhineland-Palatinate, Germany

Crystal perfection is not the only quality sought by mineral collectors. This 2 millimeter haüyne crystal is far from perfect, yet it is gemmy and alive with a variety of interesting features. Blue minerals are not really rare, but the softness of the blue in this mineral is evocative. The presence of a few well-placed crystal faces makes this specimen alluring.

Amesite
Saranovskii Mine, Saranovskaya Village, Middle Urals, Russia

Transparent gem micas are always a rarity and more so if they have a beautiful color as this violet amesite does. Even the common lepidolite rarely shows gemminess and symmetrical forms. Although amesite has been known for over a century and half, there are relatively few places where is has been found subsequently. Nonetheless, the Saranovskii Mine has produced thousands of lovely specimens, but most of the specimens have tiny crystals best appreciated with a microscope. The field of view for this specimen is only 5.4 mm. An important feature of this specimen is that the terminations show a few growth irregularities showing that these are truly the growth faces on the specimen. The side view shows the typical mica layering and many mica specimens are thought to be complete, but the breakage surface looks very much like a face. Only the microscope can satisfy our curiosity to know this specimen's perfection. From the collection of Domenico Preite.

Titanite
Montenero Quarry, Onano, Viterbo Province, Latium, Italy

Titanite is yet another mineral with a wide variety of appearances. This orange brown crystal is not a *Titan* as it is less than 2 mm long, but its acute crystal shape and its transparency earn it a valued place in mineral collections.

Anatase on Clinochlore
Griesferner Glacier, Bolzano Province, Italy

Anatase is a remarkable mineral. (above) When in large size, the crystals are almost always brilliant black "spikes", but microscopic crystals have astonishing variety, both in color and in shapes. "The Alps" shared by Italy contain wonderful examples of what many think to be a "conformist" species. This photo shows a 2 mm gemmy orange crystal with outstanding luster. A. Mattiello collection.

Left: Dark brown gemmy anatase from Plattenkogel Mountain, Ankogel, Carinthia, Austria:

Pharmacosiderite
Calafuria, Livorno Province, Tuscany, Italy

Pharmacosiderite ranges in color from orange to green, but it only shows lovely hues in its tiny crystals. The field of the upper view is but 1.67 millimeters, while the detail of the same specimen below left is only 1.13 millimeters. If these crystal were larger, they would not have the delicate color they do, but would begin to approach dark green. Collection of Domenico Preite.

Vanadinite
Mibladen Mine, Midelt, Khénifra Province, Morocco

Vanadinite is one of the few minerals of great beauty that virtually every mineral collector can hope to have in their own collections. Although it is rare in volume compared to other mineral species, there are many locations for it and even the truly great large specimens are not out of reach of the determined collector. The small crystals may also be exquisite. This 2 mm vanadinite crystal on black matrix glows when back-lighted.

Linarite and Malachite
Monte Trisa, Torrebelvicino, Vicenza Province, Veneto, Italy

Photography through the close-up lens permits the choice of where the crystals are shown in a photograph. Owners of large specimens appreciate the appearance of an entire specimen along with its placement of crystals. If a large specimen has an unfavorable shape, it is sometimes possible to remove some of the matrix to achieve a more aesthetically pleasing shape. This miniature masterpiece was photographed to show the starburst of linarite which itself is intertwined with bright green malachite spheres. The field of view is only 2.31 mm.

Azurite
Calabona Mine, Alghero, Sassari Province, Sardinia, Italy

These wonderful spherical dark blue azurite clusters span across a field of 4.14 mm, yet in this tiny window, there are three copper minerals each expressing a different color. The malachite clusters are bright green, but there is a small patch of gray black tenorite touching two azurite groups in the lower right center. The tenorite's shape is reminiscent of a science fiction creature scrambling between the dark blue mounts.

Treasured Minerals

by Russ Behnke

I began mineral collecting in earnest when my father brought home a book with a fascinating watercolor of a multicolored tourmaline crystal. I wanted to find some of these crystals myself and luckily my father knew where to go. During the 1960's there were many old mines we could prospect. We traveled all over New England finding tourmaline and discovering how elusive truly fine minerals could be. Field collecting gives one a great appreciation for the rarity of a truly fine crystal specimen, and the joy of discovering one is unforgettable.

Russ Behnke

I soon went on from field collecting to studying geological engineering at the Colorado School of Mines. While there, I helped support myself by buying specimens out of old collections and selling them to the School of Mines Museum and the Denver Museum of Natural History. I also dug some specimens myself, such as the famous uraninite crystals from Topsham, Maine.

Upon graduation, I began selling minerals full time. I started to import minerals from China, even before we had diplomatic relations with that country. The first Chinese specimens of cinnabar, wolframite, fluorite, stibnite, realgar, azurite, malachite, topaz, and tourmaline came to this country through my efforts. I was also importing from Brazil, bringing in fine tourmalines and beryls.

While I have also imported minerals from Libya, South Africa, Namibia, Peru, and Pakistan, I am currently happiest with the specimens I acquire from Uruguay. The great amethyst and calcite specimens of Uruguay are truly rare, but I have been fortunate to get many, if not most, of the great specimens that were found over the last half a dozen or so years.

I have held on to many of the best specimens, even specimens going back to the 1960's. My philosophy is to buy and hold on to the best, to the extent that I can. I believe the best specimens are still underappreciated, and I have seen many collectors sell their best pieces, only to regret it soon afterwards. The best pieces are truly irreplaceable.

I serve several mineral clubs by getting them speakers for their meetings. I have also published a free eBook, *Treasured Minerals,* which I hope will help create a few new collectors. The book is the story of my life in minerals, and is illustrated with hundreds of photos of the specimens I believe are worth pursuing and owning. I hope you enjoy the photos shown in this chapter, and you will go on to view the free full eBook, *Treasured Minerals* available at my website www.russbehnke.com.

Happy collecting! Best regards, Russ Behnke

Russell Garnet

Crystals which look like highly idealized textbook drawings can be very hard to find and are a special passion of mine. This 5 cm almandine garnet crystal on a bit of pegmatite matrix epitomizes textbook perfection.

It was found in 1885 in Russell, Massachusetts by Mr. F. S. Johnson and it remained in his family until I acquired it in 1992. It is the best garnet from Russell and it was illustrated in the September, 1994 issue of *Earth,* in the 2008 garnet issue of *Extra Lapis,* and in the *Collector's Guide to Granite Pegmatites.* To appreciate, let alone own, the best is a great privilege. We are all custodians for upcoming generations.

by Russ Behnke 246

Amethyst, Deer Hill, Stow, Maine, USA

Another great New England specimen is this 6 inch tall amethyst crystal with pagoda-like form. It was collected by Cliff Trebilcock, who needed snowshoes to reach the locality, in the winter of 1967. This piece was recognized as the finest specimen from Deer Hill when it was published in *The Mineralogical Record* shortly after I acquired it in 1982. It has also been illustrated in *The Mineralogy of Maine*.

Amethyst, Deer Hill, Stow, Maine, USA

 I admire Cliff as a most persistent and determined collector, and it was his digging in 2001 which uncovered the rough for the faceted stone shown here. I acquired the rough from Cliff in 2010 and had it faceted by Dennis Creaser. This 66 carat stone may be the finest traditionally faceted stone from Deer Hill. There are only a handful of large stones which exhibit the highly coveted red and blue flashes. To own such a fine "rough and cut" pair from New England is almost unheard of.

by Russ Behnke   248

Amazonite Twin

While I was attending the Colorado School of Mines, I naturally wanted to attempt to collect amazonite. While I had some small success, I saw nothing like this at the time – even in the Mines Museum.

Fortunately, years later, this 18 cm combination of smoky quartz, amazonite, and one large Manebach twin of amazonite came my way when Bob Matuzas decided to sell me his collection. This piece was the ultimate prize of his collection. It was dug in Teller County, Colorado by the late Ray Ziegler in the 1970's. This amazonite Manebach twin is considered one of the very best known for its intense color, the size of the twin, and the association with quartz and other fine untwinned amazonite crystals.

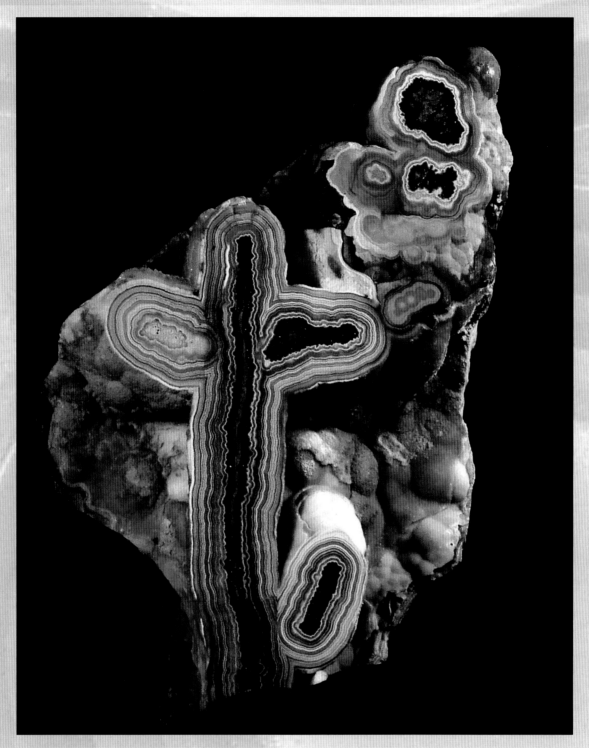

Crazy Lace Agate

My love for agates dates to the 1950's when my father brought home an agate he found in a local park. We would go collecting there in the dead of winter when the ice froze over and we could visit the island where the best agates were found.

I now have a large collection of agates from all over the world, but this 20 cm tall one is especially appealing. I had to have it as soon as I saw it illustrated in Johann Zenz's 2005 book *Agates.* It is considered the best of the crazy lace agates from Chihuahua, Mexico, and to me, it was the most striking specimen in the book. This saguaro cactus with clouds not only improbably mimics the environment that produced it, but it also makes me think of something Pablo Picasso may have painted. What more could one ask for?

Color Change Euclase

I remember seeing this Brazilian euclase during my first visit to Harvard University in the 1960's. To my mind, it was the single most remarkable specimen in the entire museum. This crystal, while only 3 cm tall, glowed with an intense emerald green color unlike anything else in the museum. My eyes were literally drawn to it from 10 meters away. There were none better known and I could only dream of owning it. Eventually, it did come my way, and it was a very good day for me. The blue color shown here shows the color under artificial light. Ouro Preto has produced many treasures, but this euclase still surpasses almost all others ever found for its luster, perfection, absolutely intense pure color, and alexandrite-like color change.

Ferrugina Tourmaline

Over the years, I imported many tourmalines and beryls directly from Brazil. One of my favorite tourmalines is this 8 cm tall crystal from the Ferrugina mine, a small working in Minas Gerais most mineral collectors have never heard of. This was the best single and only truly perfect crystal found. I like how the bright red termination contrasts with the green and watermelon sections below. This specimen is beautifully composed and is illustrated in the *Collector's Guide to Granite Pegmatites.* It is now in the Daniel J. Record collection.

by Russ Behnke 252

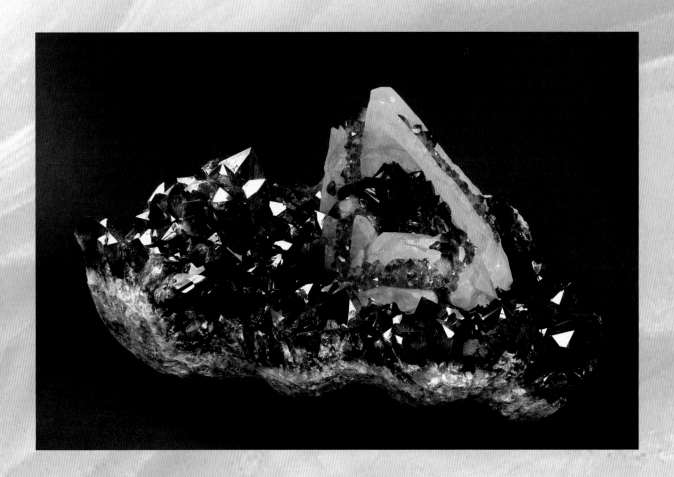

Dreamland

In 1970, my father collected some calcite crystals striped by epitaxial quartz crystals in the Cinque quarry in East Haven, Connecticut. His discovery made me want to find some myself, but it would be nearly 40 years before I was offered one. This specimen is 35 cm across with 18 cm calcite crystals striped with amethyst. Next to the calcites is a stalagmite of the richest, finest amethyst ever to come out of Santino Mine in Artigas, Uruguay. A combination such as this may only come out once in a lifetime and I have called this piece Dreamland. It is my single favorite and largest specimen. It was illustrated in *Mineral Up* magazine in 2009.

Bement's Sulfur

Clarence S. Bement, owner of the finest mineral collection of the 19th century, once treasured this 15 cm sulfur from Cianciana, Sicily. The large crystal is remarkably sharp and transparent. In 1900, the Bement Collection was given to the American Museum of Natural History in New York by J. P. Morgan, the famous philanthropist. This sulfur with its fine size and perfect provenance was a simple must have.

Azurite

In 1980, I imported 800 azurites from the new find at Shilu, Guangdong, China. This 9 cm tall specimen was the first one that I received as a sample of what was to follow. I could not believe my luck! As it turned out, however, this was the best, most lustrous, multiple rose in the entire lot. Only one other single rose had this luster, and I have kept them both all these years. While the other azurites are long gone and scattered around the world, I still have the best. Sometimes, I think I am more of an investor than a trader.

The Seaweed Pyromorphite

This 7.5 cm specimen of pyromorphite from the Daoping Mine in China has a most unusual form. Instead of the normal simple hexagonal prisms typical of pyromorphite crystals, these crystals are both twisted and bent to resemble seaweed being swept about by the tide. I acquired this in 2008 and have not seen a superior example of this strange habit.

by Russ Behnke   256

Aquamarine Cannon

I call this aquamarine "The Cannon." The larger aquamarine is 13 cm long, and the specimen was found years ago in Shigar, Pakistan. Both aquamarine crystals are doubly terminated and are in perfect condition. The aquamarines are associated with quartz, tourmaline, and feldspar in what appears to be a breccia, the result of a natural gem pocket explosion, and yet the entire specimen is in pristine condition. This specimen has perhaps the most interesting geologic past of any I own, and its form as a cannon sold me on it.

Tourmaline with Quartz

In 1993, I traded Edward E. David a great Russian gwindel for this 12.5 cm specimen from Pa-prok, Nuristan, Afghanistan. Shortly thereafter, Ed's famous first collection was acquired by the Houston Museum of Natural Science, so it seems I got this jewel just in time! I really enjoy the strong geometry of the textbook like quartz crystal which serves as backdrop for the pink elbaite and lilac lepidolite.

by Russ Behnke   258

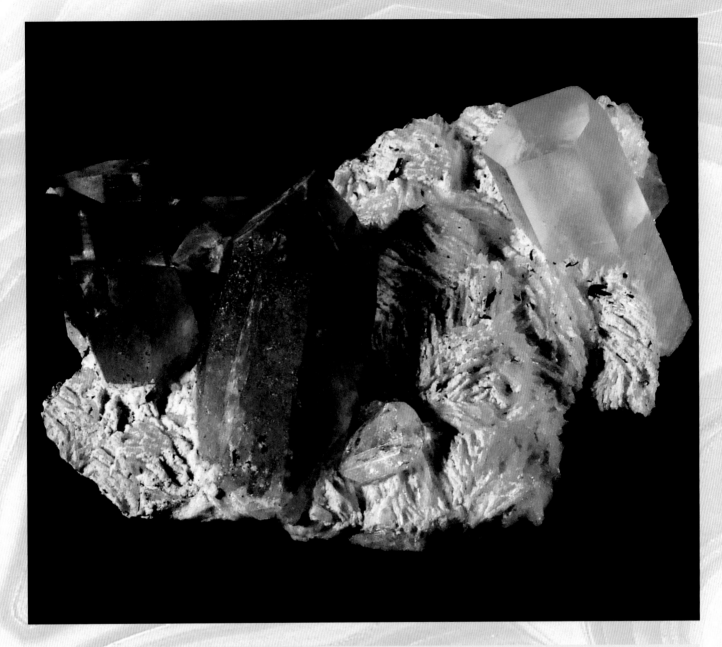

Topaz and Aquamarine

Combinations of gem crystals can be very hard to find, and I regard this 12 cm specimen from near Gilgit, Pakistan to be the Holy Grail of combinations. To find a transparent topaz with an equally transparent aquamarine is shockingly rare, and to have both quartz crystals and a contrasting feldspar matrix leaves me breathless. The odds against finding such a specimen are astronomical. The more improbable and harder to duplicate a specimen is, the more I like it. This specimen was illustrated in the *Collector's Guide to Granite Pegmatites*.

Smoky Quartz

I always enjoy showing collectors crystals the likes of which they have never seen. Quartz may be one of the most common minerals, but this 15 cm long smoky quartz from Diamantina, Brazil is exceptional, not simply because it has great color, luster, and clarity usually "reserved" for the finest specimens from Switzerland, but it also exhibits the largest "s" and "x" faces I have ever seen on a crystal of this size. This crystal is also a Dauphine twin and is textbook-like in its form.

Brazilian Amethyst

Amethyst is surely a common mineral. According to my sources, about 150,000 amethyst geodes are mined every year in South America. To find the one fine amethyst specimen that towers above the rest takes a minor miracle and years of looking. It is truly like looking for a needle in a haystack, but here is the specimen I came up with. This is an 18 cm tall specimen from Santa Catarina, Brazil. The central crystal is very large, and has just enough white on it to show it off against the surrounding crystals, all of which are perfect and finely colored. I cannot think of a finer Brazilian amethyst.

To the Moon, Alice!

Some years ago, when I was first approached by my friend Antonio to purchase minerals from Artigas, I must have rejected everything offered in the first 20 emails. But fortunately for me, I was finally offered one remarkable specimen. That one purchase allowed me to continue to purchase the best that is available from mines of Uruguay. This specimen which I have whimsically named "To the Moon, Alice!" is considered by the miners to be the best specimen found in 2009. It is 28 cm tall and makes me think of a rocket ready to be launched. It is perhaps the most sculptural specimen I own. The calcite is delicate, yet perfect, and the delicate amethyst straws are actually quartz coating thin tubes of calcite.

by Russ Behnke 262

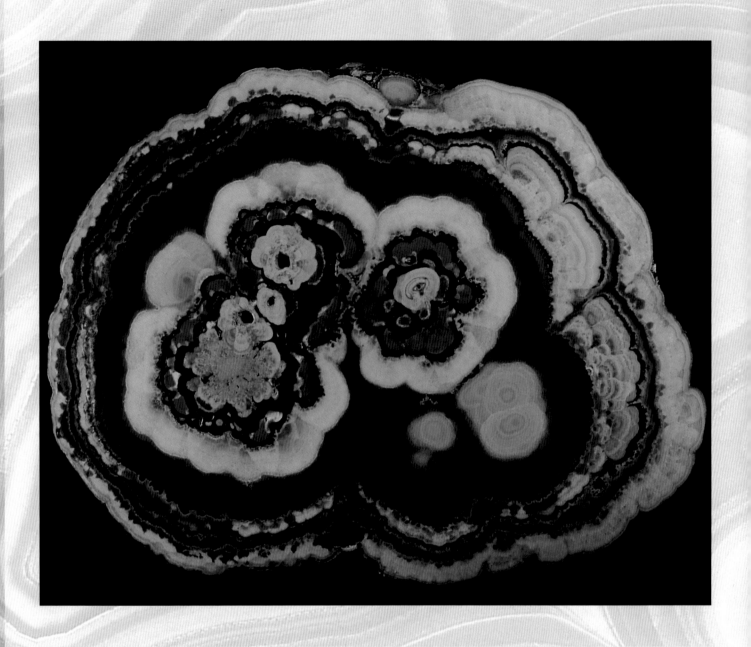

Azurite and Malachite
Morenci Mine, Morenci, Arizona, USA

Shortly after this gem material was discovered in 1884, George F. Kunz of Tiffany and Company declared this association of azurite with malachite "entirely new and one of the most beautiful ever found." This specimen from Morenci, Arizona measures 2.66 inches across and is an end slice. Very few specimens of concentric azurite and malachite have ever been found and I was lucky to acquire this one from the family of the original owner. This piece is also illustrated in *Gemstones* by Hurrell and Johnson.

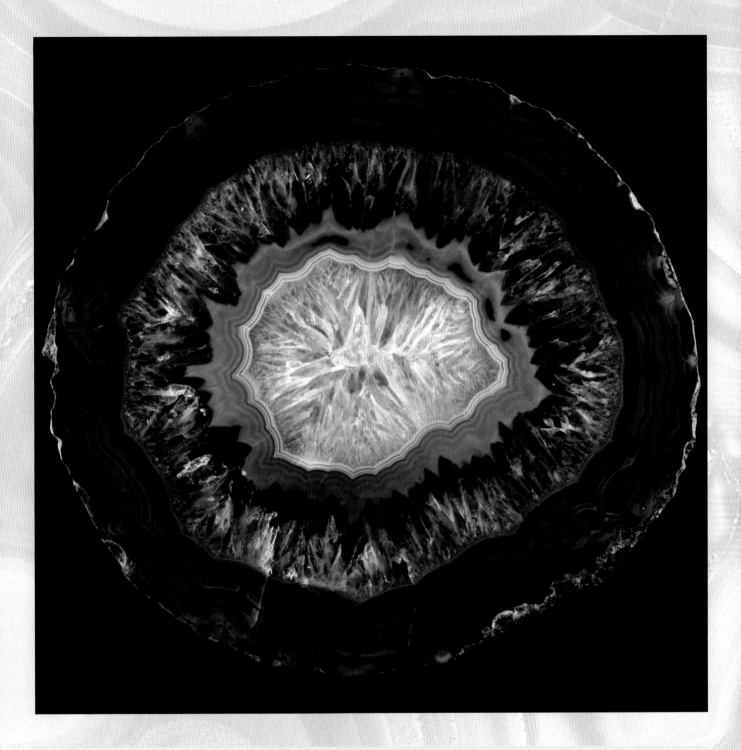

Paradise Island Agate
Condor Agate Beds, Mendoza, Argentina

According to noted collector David P. Wilber, the former owner of this specimen, this 19 cm (7.25 inch) agate is the largest known fine quality Condor Agate from Argentina. I love how the quartz in this piece rhythmically varies between beautifully colored cryptocrystalline fortifications and coarsely crystalline spikes. Few fine agates show these floating atoll-like centers, and this one is especially reminiscent of an exotic, tropical island paradise.

Chapter Eleven: *Growing Up with Minerals*
by Val Collins and Jeff Collins

Val started collecting minerals much later than the majority of the people in this wonderful compilation of world-wide collectors. He started serious collecting at the age of 34, with his first collecting trip as a member of the Fulton County Mineral Club (Gloversville, New York) to the Francon Quarry (in Montreal, Quebec) and the following day to nearby Mont St.-Hilaire. At the Francon Quarry, he found his first Weloganite, a gemmy yellow crystal cluster, measuring 2.1cm. in height, in a vug with Calcite crystals, the best find of the collecting group.

Val and Jeff Collins

After receiving accolades of encouragement and joking about the wonderful luck of beginners, he was truly hooked on minerals. Thus, he began collecting rare species before having acquired a first Calcite crystal or the more commonly collected species.

Fairies anyone? Rock Fairies that is. Val's two sons, Kelly (at the time eight years old) and Jeffrey (six years old) were his constant companions on mineral collecting trips during summers, as a time off for a school teacher. He would take his children to an abandoned quarry at Middleville, New York; in search of Herkimer Diamonds: wonderful, doubly terminated, clear quartz crystals occurring in one of the hardest dolostone rocks found in nature. To keep them out of harms way and busy, he would walk around, picking up large size rock chunks that had a "rattle", indicating that a quartz crystal was hidden inside. They would sit and break the chunks open with their rock hammers, finding the hidden treasures within every rock. Jeffrey, posed the big question, "Daddy how do you know which rocks have the crystals inside?" The answer that I gave was that there are Rock Fairies that reside within all the rocks of the earth and that one tells me which rocks to give to you. Thus begin the saga of the Rock Fairy, whom seemed to bless our many collecting trips over the last 32 years, with the rediscovery of a few lost or depleted mineral localities within my home state. The passion for mineralogy even led to a hobby becoming a business, first part-time during a teaching career and full-time in retirement. Every parent should train their children for life and it is with pride that the family tradition with natural history continues with son Jeff, who became a mineral dealer specializing in Colombian minerals and is now a partner in an emerald mine; continuing his field collecting heritage. A third generation of family mineral collectors is emerging with Val's granddaughter, Emily, who is already a participant working at mineral shows. When Emily was 2 years old, she could recognize and name five minerals, although dioptase remains her favorite species.

Fluorite
Dolomite Products Quarry, Walworth, New York, USA

Baby blue fluorite from Walworth is one of the much sought after minerals in our home state. The crystals are beautiful and they are difficult to get in good size. This one is all the more prized, as it was field collected by Jeff during the time he was going to college for his English degree after his completing his degree in business administration. 5 x 4 cm.

Cuprite
Rubtsovskoe Mine, Rudnyi Altai, Russia

This locality has set a new standard for the species, although the "classic" localities will always hold their own. These Russian cuprites are highly lustrous despite their dark color and the truly exceptional specimens such as this one never fail to dazzle the eye. 6 x 5 cm.

Atacamite Burra Burra Mine
Geweroo, New South Wales, Australia

Mineral collectors usually develop "target minerals" in their minds. With a dream speci-men in mind, it is always surprising how often one can find the "ultimate" specimen. When this atacamite presented itself, we were prepared! Of course, as social animals, we have shared our experiences with like-minded souls and our Australian friends now have it in their minds that this crystal must soon become part of their own collections. 3.5 cm x 0.8 cm. x 0.9 cm crystal and the over all size is 5 x 2.8 x 2.2 cm.

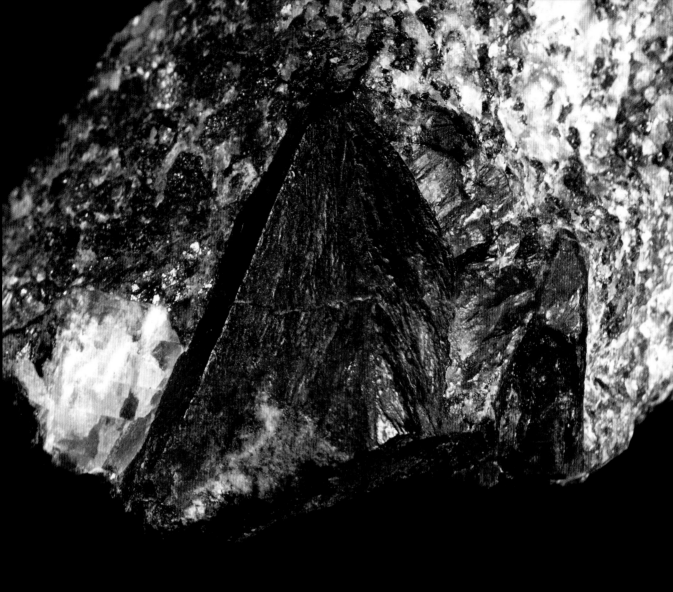

Zincite
Franklin Mine, Franklin, New Jersey, USA

Collecting minerals from Franklin can be a passion all by itself and there are many specialists in America's "First Great Mineral Locality". It is often said that no great collection of Franklin minerals can be without a fine example of each of the "Big 4": willemite, rhodonite, franklinite, and zincite. The hardest of these to acquire is a great zincite and seldom are they "available", but, again, fortune favors the prepared mind. Interestingly, this crystal was purchased in a parking lot in Tucson, Arizona during the great mineral show. By the time the deal was consummated, a cluster of the world's mineral illuminati had surrounded the specimen all cooing about this specimen's virtues. 2.5 cm x 2.0 cm and overall 5 x 3.5 x 3.5 cm. Ex: Phil Scalisi.

Cinnabar
Tongren Mine, Wanshan District, Guizhou Province, China

Cinnabar has a mystique at many levels, though its being historically a favorite ore for alchemists probably influences our ideas today. Although widespread in world occurrence, only China produced large crystals and raised the standard for quality. Unfortunately for mineral naturalists, cinnabar specimens from China disappeared from the marketplace for the better part of a century due to politics. In the 1970s, a few specimens from new discoveries began to reach the marketplace and by the 1990s, the cinnabar supply seemed endless, but it is almost always true that supplies of fine minerals are finite and new specimens are now a memory again. Of course, excellent cinnabar specimens were always uncommon and when we saw this piece, we knew that the time was ripe. 8 x 6 cm.

by Val Collins and Jeff Collins   270

Sérandite
DeMix Quarry, Mont St-Hilaire, Québec, Canada

Sérandite was originally named in whimsy, according to French mineralogists. Many new minerals were being discovered in the French colony of Guinea on Los Island in the 1920s and early 1930s and whenever there is an abundance of new minerals to name, oftentimes mineralogists become playful. During the time period, the lighthouse keeper on Los was J. M. Sérand. He was a friendly and helpful host to visiting scientists. He also had a peculiar physical feature, bright rosy cheeks and a bright rosy nose. When a bright pink mineral was found during the explorations, the mineralogists thought of their friend and sérandite was christened in his memory. Crystals of the mineral were essentially non-existent, however, but in the 1970s astonishing crystals began to be found in a quarry originally started to provide crushed stone for the Montreal World's Fair of 1967. This specimen has nearly black crystals of aegirine piercing a wonderful orange sérandite crystal, but the inside color of the sérandite is pink. 5.0 x 4.5 x 2.8 cm.

Pyrite
Muzo Mine, Boyacá Department, Colombia

Emeralds have become our passion, including minerals that have been found in emerald mines, although the variety of high-quality minerals is low. This pyrite crystal certainly rates highly among its peers despite the worldwide abundance of truly fine pyrite crystals. The charm of the specimen rests almost entirely with its departure from the ideal shape the mineral "should" have. The ridges and valleys cutting across a plane of "normal" bright faces are actually thrilling. 10 x 9 cm.

Serendibite
Mogok, Sagaing District, Mandalay Division, Burma (Myanmar)

The Collins Family mineral collection was established as a venture into nature. Because of the accident of where we lived, there was a rare mineral locality reasonably nearby, which captured our imagination, the Johnsburg, New York serendibite locality. We spent considerable effort in trying to discover what, through time, had become a "lost" locality. We canvassed the area questioning local farmers. most of whom must have felt we'd become senile. By chance, a jogger was full of information for us and we eventually experienced the thrill of finding our own serendibite crystals, although they were but millimeters in size. You can imagine that when we were presented with the opportunity to acquire a choice example of serendibite from a far off land, our hearts melted and a rare "ugly" yet so beautiful mineral joined our collection. 3.0 x 1.5 x 1.0 cm.

Boulangerite
Yaogangxian Mine, Yizhang Co., Hunan Province, China

Rare minerals have been a specialty in our collecting habits, but rare minerals usually have a limited number of fine specimens to choose from, many collectors satisfying their rare mineral interests with microscopic specimens. Boulangerite is not among the truly rare minerals, but its abundance is decidedly low and its fine specimens decidedly rare. In 2009, we were in the right place at the right time to acquire what is openly regarded as the world's best boulangerite to date. The delicacy of the crystals, which sway from the gentlest of breezes, fill us with wonder that this specimen has survived the perils of mining. Main spray is 11.5 cm, total specimen is 15 x 7 cm. Jeff Scovil photograph.

Silver
Kongsberg Mines, Buskerud, Norway

Kongsberg is the premier location for wire silver and while many specimens were produced over centuries of mining, good specimens are always scarce and always in high demand.
This fine specimen was named "The Cobra": interesting as cobras do not normally inhabit Nor-
way.10 x 5 cm. Jeff Scovil photograph.

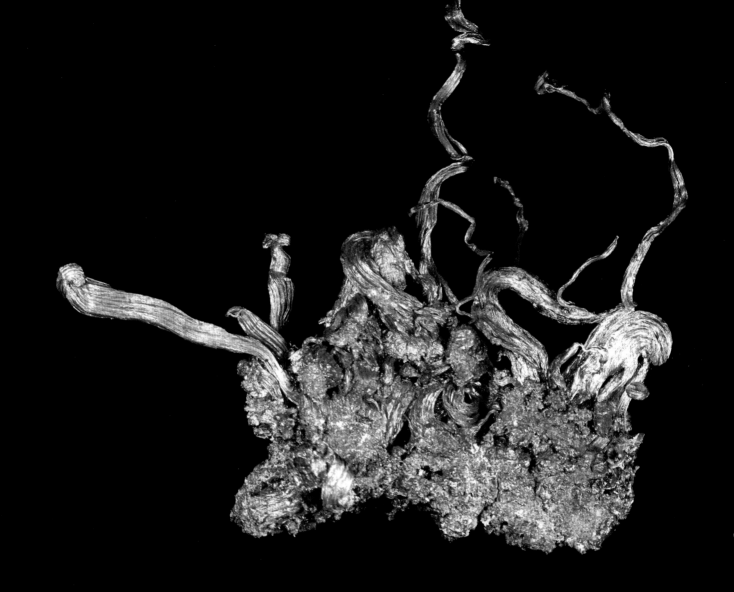

Silver with black Acanthite

Yueshan Mine, Lujiang County, Anhui Province, China

Wire silvers enjoy favored spots on our shelves. Every specimen has its own aesthetic qualities and when one chances upon a great specimen, we have to remind ourselves that even large discoveries soon become history. When there is a selection available, we know that there will be no better time than the present to get a rewarding specimen. Despite the large number of wire silver localities, specimens with writhing wires and curved ropes are always a "must have". 11 x 10 cm.

Veszelyite

Black Pine Mine, Phillipsburg, Montana, USA

Because of our interest in the rare as well as beautiful minerals, veszelyite has always been on our list of desiderata. In the early 1980s, a new find of veszelyite was news for the grapevine, but the best specimens were offered in the "West". Twenty-five years of patience were invested in order to get this one. 15 x 13 mm.

Quartz

San Cristobal Pegmatite, Santander Department, Colombia

We seem to live in an era of ever-new twinned quartz discoveries. Most finds are small, because Nature doesn't favor the obvious twins, but produces many that are subtle. The Japanese twin law was named for a late nineteenth century occurrence in Japan, which yielded a prodigious quantity of fine specimens. Previously, this style of twinning was known in southeastern France in the Alps and was called the La Gardet Twin Law. Whatever the name, we were pleased when a specimen, from one of our favorite regions, appeared. The bright orange hematite and the secondary crystals on the twin faces more than whispered to us. 9 x 8 cm.

by Val Collins and Jeff Collins 278

I started collecting minerals as a 14 year-old boy. My first field trips were with my parents in the Swiss Alps, Grisons, Valais, and Lengenbach. In addition to the Swiss Alps, famous German locations such as Hagendorf-Süd, the Clara Mine in the Black Forest, and the Eifel volcanic district were important field trips for me.

I soon realized that after having my first car and a driver's license, I could visit these localities by myself. Until then I had been depending on my parents or other mineral collectors. Because of my dependence, field trips didn't happen frequently. Unfortunately for me, the Hagendorf pit was permanently flooded in 1984, two years before I became 18 years old. Hagendorf is the biggest phosphate-bearing pegmatite in Central Europe, and its mineralization is unique and outstanding. Nonetheless, I developed a big interest in Hagendorf minerals, particularly the phosphates, and my interest in them has lasted more than 30 years.

Hagendorf minerals are frequently described in publications, but well-photographed specimens always have been rare. All of the minerals shown in my Hagendorf gallery are classed as "micromount" size, but not all are phosphates. Micromount minerals require magnification, optimally viewed with a microscope rather than a hand lens, to be well-appreciated. For the most part, the great variety of phosphate minerals, worldwide, also requires magnification for the best viewing.

Stephan Wolfsried

Some phosphate minerals such as fluorapatite, brazilianite, or pyromorphite might occur in big enough sizes so that they are "displayable", but of the 800 or so phosphate minerals, about 780 are found only as masses or in microscopic crystals. Despite the disadvantage of size, micromount size phosphate minerals are frequently beautiful, occur in more abundance than display sized specimens of their kind, and frequently occur in higher quality than bigger specimens.

All of these specimens are very small details of larger specimens and for this reason; the field of view left to right dimensions are given. All of the images in this gallery are from my collection and were photographed by me.

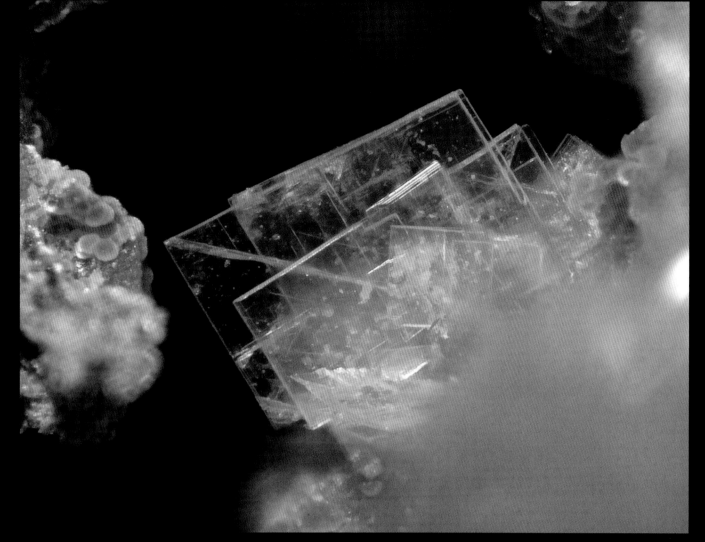

Upper View: Typical square tablets of greenish yellow **Autunite** crystals on albite with a small amount of rounded, golden yellow cacoxenite near the base.
2 x 3 mm.

Lower View: Greenish yellow **Meta-autunite** crystals on albite. Note the diagonal cleavage markings on the autunite. Most members of the Autunite Group "dehydrate" after they have been exposed to dry air. The transition may take only a few days. Such minerals with lower water contents receive the prefix "meta-" with their root name.
1.5 x 1.5 mm.

Upper View: Platy orange yellow **Bassetite** crystals. 2 x 2 mm.

Lower View: Rod-like orange **Beraunite** crystals with tan strunzite crystals and yellow stewartite. 2 x 2 mm.

Upper View: White **Benyacarite** crystals with black rockbridgeite. The crystal tablets are oblique although nearly rectangular. 2 x 2 mm.

Lower View: Green multigrowth **Chalcosiderite** crystals with orange cyrilovite on an olive green dusting of mitridatite. 2 x 2 mm.

Upper View: Reddish brown to tan **Eosphorite-Childrenite** crystal sprays. 4 x 4 mm.

Lower View: Bladed dark red **Bermanite** crystals. These are comparative giants of their species. 2 x 2 mm.

Upper View: Yellow **Cyrilovite** crystal clusters. Symmetrical crystals are pyramidal, but these crystals are so tightly intergrown the appearance is more like a spherical cluster. 2 x 3 mm.

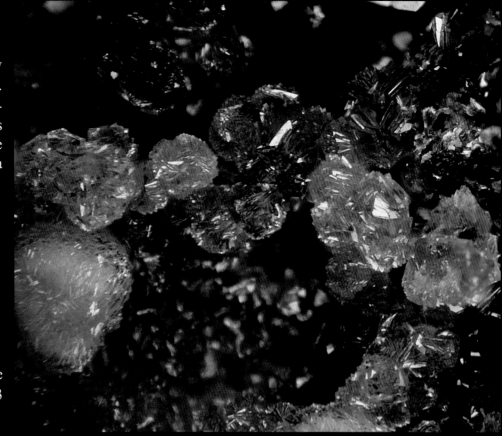

Lower View: Grayish white **Fairfieldite** sheaves. 2 x 3 mm.

Upper View: Black bladed
Columbite-(Fe) crystals in
albite. This mineral is found in
granite pegmatites around the
world, but this specimen is in
keeping with my theme of
miniature crystals. 2 x 4 mm.

Lower View:
Gray **Fluorapatite** showing
first-order prism and second-
order pyramid. 3 x 3 mm.

Hureaulite

Hureaulite is one of the very desirable phosphate species from Hagendorf. Some of the world's best specimens come from this location. Although not a record size specimen, this bright pink spray of hureaulite crystals has an aesthetic divergence, which makes this specimen a true prize. 10 x 10 mm.

Upper View: Yellow **Cacoxenite** crystal sprays. Sometimes this mineral is found in clusters which look like solid botryoids, while on rare occasions, cacoxenite specimens such as this one remind us why the famous mineralogist Rene Just Haüy called crystals the "flowers" of the mineral kingdom. 4 x 4 mm.

Lower View: Yellow **Cacoxenite** crystal tufts. This field of cacoxenite has a more normal appearance than the spectacular one above, butit still has an organic character. 4 x 4 mm.

Upper View: Acutely bladed white
Kingsmountite crystals.
3 x 3 mm.

Lower View: Brown **Keckite**
crystal group. Frequently this unusual species forms tightly clus-
tered crystals, which may be
botryoidal. 3 x 3 mm.

Upper View: Dark brown pyramidal **Landesite** crystals. 3 x 3 mm.

Lower View: Orange **Laueite** crystal with yellow acute blades of stewartite. 3 x 3 mm.

Upper View:
White **Leucophosphite** crystals with dark yellow cyrilovite.
2 x 2 mm.

Lower View: Light brownish green **Nontronite** crystal sprays. Visible crystals of clay minerals such as nontronite are very rare.
4 x 4 mm.

Upper View: White **Parascholzite** intimately intergrown in **Scholzite** crystals. The two species are indistinguishable visually. 3 x 3 mm.

Lower View: Very dark green isolated **Perloffite** crystal with quartz crystals. 1 x 1 mm.

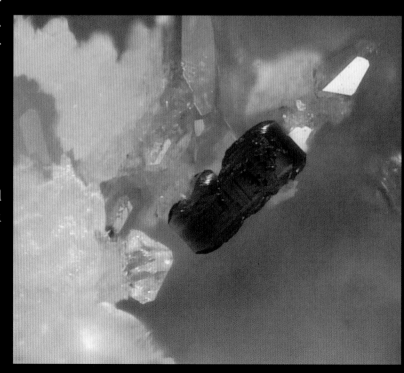

Upper View:
Greenish gray **Phosphophyllite** "heart-shaped" twin crystal. This mineral often is found with two crystals intergrown in a specific geometrical pattern. 10 x 12 mm.

Lower View: Pink bladed **Phosphosiderite** crystals. 2 x 2 mm.

by Stephan Wolfsried   292

Upper View: Yellow gemmy pseudohexagonal **Pseudolaueite** crystals on botryoidal black rockbridgeite. 3 x 3 mm.

Lower View: Brassy metallic **Pyrite** crystals. 6 x 8 mm.

Upper View: Brown scaly stalactites of **Robertsite**. The mineral usually forms dusty fine-grained coatings, but it can occasionally form crystals, which may be seen with microscopic investigation. 2 x 3 mm.

Lower View: Black **Rockbridgeite** blocky crystals in tan siderite crystal clusters. 3 x 3 mm.

by Stephan Wolfsried   294

Upper View: Brown **Schoonerite** crystal sprays with greenish gray phosphophyllite. 5 x 6 mm.

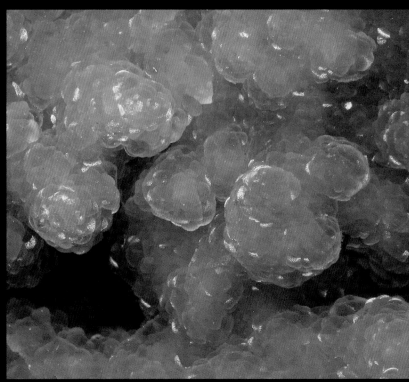

Lower View: Golden brown **Siderite** clusters. Siderite is a common host for rare minerals at Hagendorf. 6 x 6 mm.

Upper View: Golden Yellow acutely bladed **Stewartite** crystals. 3 x 3 mm.

Lower View: Purple gemmy **Strengite** crystal. 6 x 8 mm.

Upper View: Pinkish purple botryoidal **Strengite** crystals. Tight groupings of crystals are frequently seen in this species. 4 x 4 mm.

Lower View: Pale tan straw-yellow **Strunzite** crystals. 7 x 9 mm.

Upper View: Green **Torbernite/Metatorbernite** crystal on quartz. Similarly to autunite, torbernite may dehydrate slightly forming metatorbernite. 3 x 3 mm.

Lower View: Orange clusters of **Uranosphaerite** crystals. 3 x 3 mm.

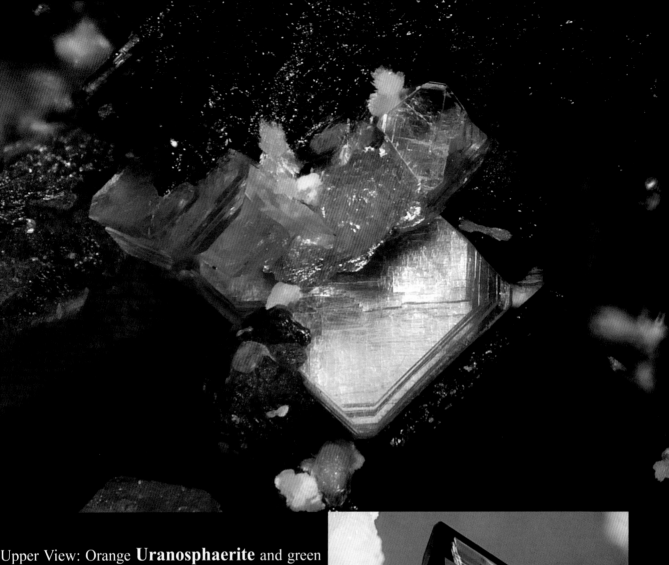

Upper View: Orange **Uranosphaerite** and green Metatorbernite crystals. 2 x 3 mm.

Lower View: Blue violet **Vivianite** crystal. 3 x 3 mm.

Whitmoreite

Whitmoreite frequently shows botryoidal grouping with several elongated crystals of the same mineral projecting from the core. These are typical clusters of brown to golden yellow botryoidal whitmoreite with minor light olive green mitridatite and black rockbridgeite. 3 x 3 mm.

Earlshannonite

Light brown to golden yellow **Earlshannonite** crystals showing the so-called "water-mines" habit. The mineral formed a botryoidal core of same-size crystals with an overgrowth of more individually placed elongated crystals. Earlshannonite is the manganese-rich "relative" of whitmoreite. 3 x 4 mm.

Wilhelmvierlingite

Orange brown rectangular **Wilhelmvierlingite** crystals with small black rockbridgeite crystals. This species is somewhat elusive and most specimens of this rare mineral show very poor crystal shapes. 2 x 3 mm

The Beginning of this Section Features
Zeolites and Minerals Commonly Found with Zeolites

Apophyllite, Nasik, India. (upper left) Two green apophyllites on stilbite. Specimen measures 11.4 cm tall and 8.9 cm wide. Joe Budd photograph.

Apophyllite, Nasik, India. (upper right) Here we see a bicolor crystal (6.4 cm across by 3.8 cm thick), approaching a "cubic" shape. Specimen measures 7 cm wide and 5 cm tall. Joe Budd photograph.

Apophyllite, Jalgaon, India. (lower left) Green, oval Apophyllite cluster on peach-colored plate of small stilbites. Specimen measures 15.2 cm x 12.7 cm high. Joe Budd photograph.

Apophyllite, Pune, India. (upper right) Green and gemmy apophyllite crystals on a flat, white plate measuring 14 cm wide and 10.2 cm high. Joe Budd photograph.

Apophyllite, Jalgaon, India. (lower right) Seen here are two different colorful species in a beautiful arrangement: light green apophyllites sitting on the clusters of peach-colored stilbites. Specimen measures 12.7 cm wide and 16.5 cm tall. Joe Budd photograph.

by Keith Proctor and Mauna Proctor   304

Apophyllite with Stilbite, Jalgaon, India. (upper right) A cluster of colorless apophyllites crystallized in a most unusual shape. It is a narrow arch with the two sides almost meeting and the apophyllites do touch where the single peach-colored stilbite bridges the gap. Specimen measures 12.7 cm high by 7 cm wide at the widest point. Van King photograph.

Apophyllite Jalgaon, India. (lower left) We see here a flower cluster of gemmy, colorless crystals. Specimen measures 10.8 cm high by 7 cm wide. Jeff Scovil photograph.

Apophyllite with Stilbite, Jalgaon, India. (lower right) Apophyllite with peach-colored stilbites on a chalcedony stalk. Specimen measures 10.2 cm wide by 8.9 cm deep. Joe Budd photograph.

Apophyllite, Ahmed Nagar Quarry, Maharashtra, India. (upper left) Pictured here is a green apophyllite specimen from the Ahmad Nagar discovery, which occurred when a farmer named Ahmed Nagar was digging a well. Instead, he hit one of the wonderful green apophyllite deposits and he became rich and famous . This specimen measures 20.3 cm wide by 17.8 cm high. Joe Budd photograph.

View B. (lower right) Apophyllite "Flower Cluster" crystal spray. If we look on the bottom right corner of this specimen, we see a beautiful radiating cluster of delicate green apophyllite crystals, which measure 5.7 cm wide. Joe Budd photograph.

(above) **Apophyllite, Ahmed Nagar, India.** (lower left) Seen here is a radiating cluster of green Apophyllite crystals. These are flat tipped crystals. Specimen measures 4.4 cm wide and 4.4 cm high. Joe Budd photograph.

Okenite, Bombay, India. (upper right)
Many Zeolite specimens feature open
basalt geodes, which were carved out of
a solid rock, pillow lava, by the talented
and supremely patient stone carvers of
India. This 8.9 cm wide, open basalt
geode features especially fuzzy Okenite
balls. Joe Budd photograph.

Epistilbite, Bombay, India . Epistilbites in
big peach-colored crystals, as seen here, are
rare. This "clamshell" open basalt geode
boasts many crystals and it measures 14 cm
wide, 5.7 cm high and 5.7 cm deep.
Joe Budd photograph.

Okenite, Bombay, India. (lower right) This geode
seems to be a garden of okenite "mushrooms" in a
cave.. Specimen measures 17.8 cm wide by 7.5 cm
high.

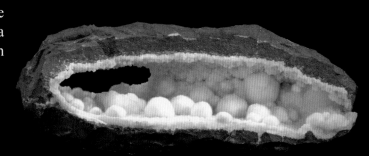

Prehnite Casts After Laumontite with Apophyllite and Mordenite, Bombay, India. (upper right) These prehnite spires are arranged in a very pleasing jackstraw fashion and dispersed over the surface of these spires are small white clusters of mordenite crystals, along with minute colorless apophyllites giving added sparkle to this specimen. Specimen measures 11.4 cm wide, 11.4 cm high.
Joe Budd photograph.

Prehnite Casts After Laumontite with Apophyllite and Mordenite, Bombay, India. (lower left) Here we see another group of hollow Prehnite spires, some of which still have laumontite crystals encased in their prehnite cocoons. Unlike the specimen above, most of these prehnite tubes are open and empty. Specimen measures 15.2 cm x 12.7 cm high.
Joe Budd photograph.

Mesolite and Apophyllite, Pashan Quarry, Pune, India. (upper right) Here we see a white mesolite crystal spray with a 7.5 cm wide cluster of square-shaped needles. This "pincushion" cluster is sitting on top of a stack of bright green apophyllite crystals. This specimen measures 8.9 cm wide, 10.2 cm tall and 8.3 cm thick. Joe Budd photograph.

Apophyllite with Mesolite, Pune, India. (lower left) This is a magnificent white mesolite specimen with small, white stilbites, and on the left side we see a dark green crystal of apophyllite. This is a visually pleasing specimen, because of the arrangement of these three species. This assemblage measures 16.5 cm wide and is 7.5 cm deep. Joe Budd photograph.

Heulandite, Nasik, India. Pictured here is a beautiful light mauve heulandite. Three stilbite crystals are growing out of the front left side face of this huge heulandite, measuring 10.8 cm long and standing 5 cm high (thick). This crystal is perched on a matrix of small quartz crystals. Joe Budd photograph.

Heulandite, Jalgaon, India. (lower left) The main pure white crystal measures 7.5 cm long and 3.8 cm wide. Note that this crystal is nestled on top of a bed of quartz crystals. Specimen measures 8.9 cm wide and 7.5 cm tall. Joe Budd photograph.

Heulandite on Quartz, Jalgaon, India. (lower right) Pictured here is a peach-colored heulandite (7.5 cm long), and it's perched on a matrix made up of short quartz stalks, with minute, pale-colored, thin heulandites also sitting on the quartz stalks. 10.2 cm tall and 7.4 cm wide. Joe Budd photograph.

Heulandite, Jalgaon, India. (upper right) Seen here is a nice specimen displaying two brilliant crystals of orange-pink heulandite, forming, what appear to be, two butterfly wings. The basalt matrix is sprinkled with peach-colored stilbites. Specimen measures 8.9 cm wide and 6.4 cm deep. Joe Budd photograph.

Heulandite on Chalcedony with Stilbites, Jalgaon, India. Heulandite cannot be identified by color as the examples show. This combination shows reddish colored heulandite specimens intermixed with isolated, pale peach-colored stilbite crystals, with both species being perched on top of inch long, white chalcedony stalks. This matrix is a concave, one-third open, basalt geode/vug and measures 15.2 cm long and 10.2 cm high, with the biggest heulandite measuring 4.4 cm long, by 1.9 cm high. Joe Budd photograph.

Heulandite, Jalgaon, India. (lower right) It is noteworthy that in the heulandite species there is a great profusion of colors, all of which are caused by different colored compounds that got trapped in the crystal structure. Specimen measures 5 x 6 cm.
Jeff Scovil photograph.

Stilbite "Bowties", Jalgaon, India. Pictured here are two perfect 7.5 cm wide, "bowtie"-shaped stilbite crystals, each sitting on matrix. The white crystal (#1) and the reddish crystal (#2), which was possibly stained by red hematite, make a perfect matched pair. Joe Budd photograph.

Apophyllite with Stilbite, Jalgaon, India. (lower views) This specimen on the left (#3) displays a 6.4 cm long, doubly terminated colorless apophyllite crystal being penetrated by a 5 cm, peach-colored stilbite crystal. Both the gem apophyllite crystal and the stilbite are perched on a 5.7 cm high, colorless apophyllite stalk. Joe Budd photograph.

Stilbite and Apophyllite, Jalgaon, India. On the right is a 7 cm long, peach-colored, "Bowtie" stilbite, sitting crosswise and embedded in a 8.9 cm high, colorless apophyllite stalk, which is 2.5 cm wide. Joe Budd photograph.

Chalcedony with Stilbite And Calcite, Jalgaon, India. (left) We see here three chalcedony stalks intergrown at right angles to each other with rhombohedral calcite on the tip of each chalcedony stalk. All this assemblage is covered with small, delicate stilbite crystals, producing a rare presentation. Almost 12.7 cm tall. Joe Budd photograph.

Red Hematite Stained Stilbite on Apophyllite, Nasik, India. (lower right) Red highlights on stilbite crystal, due to dusty hematite, sits on a stack of blocky-shaped, pale yellow apophyllites. Specimen measures 14.6 cm wide and 7.5 cm tall. Lynn Sim photograph.

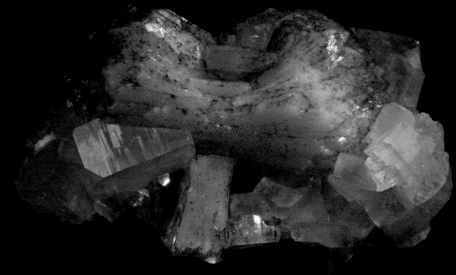

Scolecite on A Stilbite Matrix, Bombay, India.
This wonderfully aesthetic, head-shaped spray of
scolecite measures 14 cm by 14 cm, and sits on a
mostly hidden cluster of cream colored stilbite
crystals. This fun composition specimen suggesting a cartoon view of "bad hair on a windy day"
also has very flat and thin scolecites.
Jeff Scovil photograph

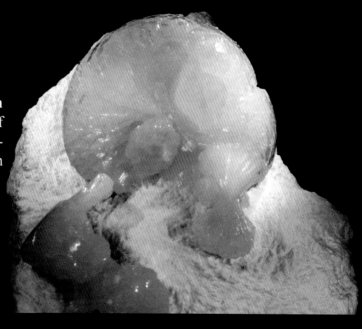

**Stellerite Doughnut To Bowtie Crystal Shapes on
Laumontite, Aurangabad, India.** This cluster of
doughnut--shaped and bowtie-shaped crystals measures 10.2 cm tall by 7.5 cm deep. The rims of both
crystal types are very glassy appearing.
Van King photograph

Thomsonite.Aurangabad, Maharashtra, India. (left)
Thomsonite is an uncommon zeolite. This flat basalt matrix measures 16.5 cm wide by 12.7 cm tall. This is a wonderful example of the species. Joe Budd photo

Many collectors fall in love with minerals that are from a particular chemical group. These collectors usually do not know much about chemistry, but use the names of the mineral classes as a way of searching for minerals they intuitively enjoy. For example, the carbonates include popular minerals such as: Calcite, Azurite, Malachite, Smithsonite, Rhodochrosite, Siderite, Cerussite, Strontianite, and Aragonite. The silicates were shown in Chapter One and the beginning of this chapter. These species are relatively common and sometimes are available in beautiful specimens. Some collectors like to have a very specific collection of only calcite or only azurite, because something about those minerals appeals to them. We've simplified this kind of collecting by thinking of the "-ates". The common "-ates", of interest to mineral collectors are: arsenates, carbonates, chromates, molybdates, phosphates, silicates, sulphates, and tungstates, and there are several additional "-ates", which collectors enjoy. This suffix simply signifies that oxygen is an important component, with a particular constant ratio, in the mineral's make up.

Oftentimes, the mineral localities that are within realistic traveling distances produce certain "ates" in abundance and a collector may specialize in what they may find. However, collectors also collect certain specialties for reasons they themselves cannot express. Other popular "-ate" species include. Barite, Gypsum, Anglesite, Celestine or even rare species such as Creedite or Posnjakite/Langite. The arsenates, vanadates, and phosphates are particularly popular as so many of them are colorful. Molybdates, chromates, and tungstates are also very desirable, but have more rare minerals than some of the other "-ates". We will start with calcite,

one of the most popular "-ates" and will continue with these minerals in a large section of our gallery. In particular, we are fascinated by the forms that minerals take and the calcites we'll show are arranged according to particular styles or "habits" as they are so-called. We will start with very pointed crystals - called scalenohedrons, so-called because each face is a scalene triangle. There are similar calcite crystals which are "pointed", but, which have few faces and are steep rhombohedrons. Careful examination is sometimes necessary to tell them apart.

Calcite, Elmwood Mine, Carthage, Tennessee, USA. (right) Many collectors consider the Elmwood calcites to be the world's most beautiful for the species. Here we see a superb Elmwood calcite, which was acquired from the famous Dr. Steve Neely collection in Tennessee. The main gemmy, twinned, and doubly terminated crystal is 14.6 cm long, and sits on matrix. Specimen measures 19.7 cm high. Joe Budd photograph.

When we discuss calcite crystal formation we must mention that although there are more than 2200 different known combinations in calcite crystallization, there are essentially only three basic calcite crystal types.

(1) Scalenohedrons pointed crystals that generally have tapered sides going toward the tip.

(2) Hexagonal Prisms which have parallel sides leading towards the tip. These hexagonal crystal tops usually have three-faceted, pointed "Mercedes-symbol" terminations.

(3) Rhombohedrons are the bulbous, blocky, flattened or twisted-shaped crystals which usually have the diagnostic three-faceted so-called "Mercedes-symbol" terminations somewhere on their crystal faces, but they may also be very elongated and pointed. Rhombohedrons are generally not confused with the pointed scalenohedrons or hexagonal prism crystal types, although many calcite specimens display two or even all three of these familiar crystal habits.

Four of the seven carbonate species shown in this collection. Calcite, smithsonite, rhodochrosite, and siderite crystallize in the trigonal (meaning three types) crystal system. Two chemically related minerals, aragonite and smithsonite, belong to the orthorhombic crystal system and have very different crystal shapes than those shown by the calcite group.

Calcite, Elmwood Mine, Carthage, Tennessee, USA. This 8.9 cm long gemmy single calcite crystal perched on a small white matrix of strontium-rich barite is a jewel: compact, totally gemmy, doubly terminated, and features well defined crystal faces. From the Dr. Steve Neely collection, Tennessee. Specimen measures 9.5 cm x 4.4 cm. Joe Budd photograph.

twinning plain in the center of the crystal as seen here. Another desirable quality of Elmwood calcites is their gemmy character. Of course, the gem crystals are the most highly coveted and sought after. This beautiful crystal is perched on a matrix of strontium-rich barite crystals. Specimen measures 12.7 cm high by 8.9 cm wide.

Jeff Scovil photograph.

Calcite, Irai, Brazil. This calcite "flower blossom" specimen is a favorite. The arrangement and presentation of these six "flower clusters" perched on a thin basalt matrix is magnificent and almost defies description in beauty, perfection and overall eye appeal. Many other smaller green-stained calcite crystals act as the garden surrounding these clusters. Specimen measures 6.75" by 12.7 cm. Joe Budd photograph.

Calcite, Irai, Brazil. The second "flower cluster" specimen from the diggings at Irai, Brazil is stained green by the mineral celadonite mica trapped inside the crystal. The calcite overgrowth was not sufficient to complete a "cocoon", and exposed celadonite shows in the center crystals. The same calcite microcrystals coat this matrix "garden", adding contrast and delicacy. Specimen measures 7.5" x 11.4 cm x 12.7 cm. Joe Budd photograph.

The third "flower cluster" specimen also comes from the mines at Irai, Brazil. It took many years of searching to find these three complimentary specimens. This basalt matrix hosts five white "flower blossom" clusters. Specimen measures 20.3 cm x 12.7 cm. All three of these Irai specimens display blunt terminations showing the classic rhombohedral, three-faceted, "Mercedes-symbol" terminations. Joe Budd photograph.

Calcite, Irai, Brazil. (left) This huge cluster of eight very elongated, bone-white calcite scalenohedral crystals with side branches is an artistically balanced composition. Overall form, balance, rhythm and symmetry are very important to crystal beauty and value. Specimen measures 17.1 cm wide x 12.7 cm high. All photographs on this page by Joe Budd

The first four miniature-sized calcite flower specimens below demonstrate the great variety of colors yielded by the cavernous basalt lava geodes of the famous Irai mining area.

The last "miniature" (miniature means that it will fit into a 5 cm cube) is the so-called Cactus Calcite, which, appropriately, came either from Arizona or Mexico.

Calcite, Gongcheng, China. (above left) This 27.9 cm by 7.5 cm symmetrical arrangement of sharp-pointed calcite crystals appears to be a cudgel to cause great damage to an opponent.

(above middle) This is an "Icicle" calcite. This is another redissolved specimen, meaning it went partially into and out of solution during formation. It displays a multitude of unusual facets and even looks as if it were wet and melting and about to drip. This mine is nearest the famous Guilin city in the center of the mysterious "upside down cone-shaped mountain" region cut by the famous Lei river and presenting some of China's most beautiful scenery. This specimen measures 19 cm long and 1.9 cm wide.

Calcite Crystals on Calcite Stalk, Gongcheng, China. (above right) This hexagonal prism calcite features a bizarre and rare shape. Dr. Professor Liu in Germany states that only a "few" specimens of this configuration were harvested in China. These "palm frond" calcites with parallel faces leading up to the tips are hexagonal prisms. Both the calcite crystals and the calcite coating on the stalk are translucent and beautifully striated. The "palm frond" crystals are very slightly tapered. Specimen measures 13.3 cm tall. Joe Budd photographs.

Calcite, 884 Mine, Leiping, China. Note the unusual Calcite crystallography here. A so-called butterfly twin crystals featuring two twinned rhombohedrons are arranged like butterfly wings. (Note the three faces instead of six faces.) This discovery occurred in 1998 and specimens such as this one were featured in Professor Dr. Liu's definitive book, *Fine Minerals of China*. About this discovery he says "…these butterfly twins raised the price of calcite specimens to a new high in the international market." Specimen measures 5 cm by 5 cm. Van King photograph.

Calcite with Amethyst Irai, Brazil. (lower left) This calcite specimen consists of two fat, blunt tipped cream-colored scalenohedrons, both of which are skirted with a sheath of pretty Amethyst Quartz crystals. on the left side of the left crystal we see a series of small flattened rhombohedrons sticking out in tiers. This suggests to us that the pointed scalenohedrons crystallized at a higher temperature than the flat, partial rhombohedrons. Specimen measures 11.4 cm x 11.4 cm. Joe Budd photograph.

Calcite, Guangxi Province China. (above) Very unusual calcite crystals stained red by hematite inclusions. Joe Budd photograph.

Calcite on Amethyst Quartz, Irai, Brazil. (lower right) Four pale yellow scalenohedral Calcite crystals flare off a vertical stack of amethyst crystals. This is a good example of nice color contrast and size ratios between crystals and matrix and overall composition. Specimen measures 15.2 cm tall by 12.7 cm wide. Joe Budd photograph.

Calcite, Baoshan Prefecture, Yunnan Province, China. This specimen features 20 huge white elongated cone-shaped calcite crystals with their crystals sprouting outward from the base. The centers of these 20 cone calcites are partially hollow. This formation is a visual feast. Specimen measures 25.4 cm high by 27.9 cm wide. Jeff Scovil photograph.

Calcite, Jalgaon, India. (upper right)
This is a gemmy bulbous, highly striated rhombohedral-shaped calcite crystal. This pale yellow gem crystal was found in the basalt lava flows and sits on peach-colored stilbite crystals. Note the 5 cm x 5 cm x 5 cm three-faceted termination on the very top of the front face. This is diagnostic for a basic rhombohedral termination. This specimen measures 12.7 cm tall, 12.7 cm high and 8.9 cm thick.
Joe Budd photograph.

Calcite, Jalgaon, India. This gemmy yellow rhombohedron presents a very blocky shape and exhibits highly striated faces on the lower right and top left behind two perfect, completely gemmy yellow interpenetration twin rhombohedrons. This is a textbook example for this crystal habit, but the three-faceted rhombohedron is not so obvious. To see the rhomb faces clearly, one must look straight on at any of the sharp corners of this crystal comparing these to the rhombic faces in the previous specimens. Specimen measures 12.7 cm x 10.8 cm x 7.5 cm thick.
Joe Budd photograph.

Calcite, Rudniy, Kazakhstan. Calcite rhombohedrons from Rudniy have intricate surface linings. They also seem to glow with their own inner light. Specimen measures 7 cm wide, 5 cm deep and 5 cm tall.
Joe Budd photograph.

Calcite Twins on Stilbite and Apophyllite, Jalgaon, India. (upper right) These crystals, display water clear interpenetration calcite twins perched on top of a zeolite matrix. Specimen measures 11.4 cm x 8.9 cm.
Joe Budd photograph.

Calcite, Rudniy, Kazakhstan. (lower left) The lines on this cluster of four intergrown (interpenetration twinned) rhombohedrons are even more pronounced and beautiful than on the specimen above. Specimen measures 6.4 cm wide by 3.8 cm tall.
Joe Budd photograph.

Calcite, Edong Mining District, China. This amazing and sculptural single red (hematite-stained) crystal sits on a perfectly sized matrix is the best from its pocket and was hand carried all the way from China to the United States. Specimen measures 10.2 cm high x 8.9 cm wide with a 7.5 cm by 7.5 cm main crystal. Joe Budd photograph.

Calcite, China. 17.8 cm tall and 4.4 cm wide. The front face of this rhombohedron is diamond-shaped, as are the rhombohedral faces on the specimen on the right. Joe Budd photograph.

Calcite on Chalcedony, Jalgaon, India. This 20.3 cm tall Calcite/Stilbite/Quartz specimen came from the "pillow" lava flows of the Jalgaon quarries. On top of this statuesque pillar of chalcedony is a perfect 6.4 cm tall rhombohedron of calcite facing exactly the same as the top rhombohedron on the previous specimen including the diamond -shaped front face. Much of this specimen is enhanced by peach-colored stilbites sprinkled over both the stalk and calcite.
Joe Budd photograph.

Calcite with Hematite Staining, Nandan Co., Hechi Prefecture, Guangxi Zhuang Autonomous Region, China. These rhombohedral calcite crystals are 10.2 cm tall and 10.2 cm wide forming a pyramid display and have a brilliant red color from hematite staining, both on the surface and internally. Each of the three crystal sides has a multitude of stunning 0.6 cm to 3.2 cm long red rhombohedrons protruding from its face. All these calcite varieties illustrate the tremendous flexibility and diversity of the species.
Lynn Sim photograph.

Calcite with Red Hematite, 884 Mine, China. (lower right) This 12.7 cm tall by 9.5 cm wide cluster of three-faceted rhombohedral tips is similar to the previous specimen with either one or two of their three sides stained red with selective deposition of hematite. Acquired from Dr. Liu's China collection, and pictured on page 192 of his iconic book entitled *Fine Minerals of China*. Joe Budd photograph.

Calcite, Turt Mine, Near Cavnic, Romania. (upper right) Further illustrating the flexibility of calcite's crystal habits, this rhombohedral calcite grew very flat. However, an optical illusion is so perfect that this calcite crystal looks like a square box. In reality, while it is almost 5 cm across, it is only 1.6 cm thick! This perfect single crystal, perched on drusy quartz matrix, is an flat rhombohedron displaying the three-faceted "Mercedes-symbol" termination. Specimen measures 10.2 cm wide, 6.4 cm tall. Joe Budd photograph.

Calcite, Jinglong Mine, China. (lower left) This charming calcite specimen is another one-of-a-kind example featuring two vertical stacks of flat pale green rhombohedrons. This structure gives an interesting appearance, looking like a stack of miniature Chinese hats. Specimen measures 14 cm wide, 14 cm tall and 10.2 cm deep. Joe Budd photograph.

Calcite with Red Hematite Staining, Jinlong Mine, China.
(upper right) This specimen exhibits a 8.3 cm tall, rlightly ed stained steep rhombohedron covered with a flat, 4.4 cm wide rhombohedron sitting on top. Three vertical edges separating the three sides of this rhombohedron have flat, wafer-like rhombohedrons sticking out all the way to the top flat rhombohedron. No wonder calcite is one of the TOP TEN species with collectors. Unlike man-made paintings and sculptures, no two specimens, even from the same pocket, are identical, yet they may show a resemblance to each other.
Joe Budd photograph.

Calcite, Leiping mine, Hunan Province, China. (on the left) This calcite specimen was trying to do the same thing as the one above. This crystal seems to have a hematite colored phanton and clear to cloudy white calcite grew over it. Specimen measures 7.5 cm tall.
Jeff Scovil photograph.

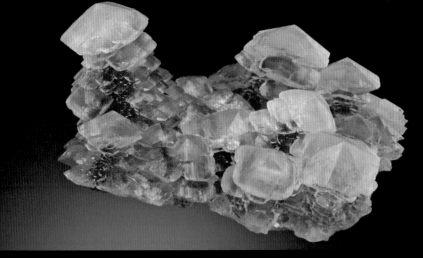

Calcite, Leiping, China. (above) Clusters of Chinese Hat calcite showing red color phantoms. Specimen measures 17.8 cm wide by 10.2 cm deep.
Jeff Scovil photograph.

Calcite, China. (center right) The 1st growth phase on this specimen was a stack of Rhombohedrons. The 2nd growth phase was a coating with red limonite staining, and 3rd is a thin, colorless growth phase on top. Specimen measures 9.5 cm high by 10.2 cm wide.
Joe Budd photograph.

Calcite, China. (lower left) These crystals formed in a stibnite-producing location and the dark markings inside the crystals are oriented stibnite inclusions. As the calcite grew, it enclosed the stibnite. The biggest rhomb is 5.7 cm wide and 1.9 cm thick. China is indeed the iconic locality for unique non-gem specimens. Probably from Xikuangshan Sb deposit, Lengshuijiang Co., Loudi Prefecture, Hunan Province, China. Specimen measures 22.9 cm wide and 11.4 cm high. Joe Budd photograph.

Calcite, Cavnic, Romania. (left) These roof-shape forms are flat to twisted saddle-shapes of white calcite rhombohedrons. Specimen measures 14 cm wide by 16.5 cm high.
Joe Budd photograph.

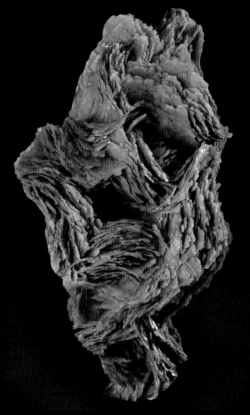

Calcite, China. (upper right) These brown, flat, tightly compacted rhombohedrons are twisted into wave-like or saddle-shaped crystals. Specimen measures 7.5 cm wide and 15.2 cm high, with 5 cm 6.4 cm wide.
Joe Budd photograph.

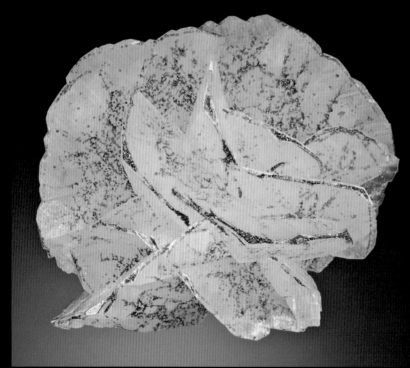

Calcite, Chenzhou Prefecture, Hunan Province, China. (lower left) This beautiful 10.2 cm wide and 9.5 cm high cluster of flat and twisted rhombohedrons (some 7.5 cm across) is loosely arranged into a flower cluster. The enticing detail about these white crystals is the narrow rims densely inlaid with minute pyrite crystals. These lines define each flat and twisted rhombohedral crystal.
Jeff Scovil photograph.

Calcite, Nikolai Mine, Dal'negorsk, Russia. Pink (manganese rich) manganocalcite in flat and twisted, tightly compacted rhombohedrons forming a "flower" arrangement. This 8.9 cm wide and 6.4 cm high pink manganocalcite "flower cluster"sits on a tall matrix of minute tan calcite rhombohedrons. Specimen measures 10.2 cm wide and 15.2 cm tall and 3.8 cm thick. Joe Budd photograph.

Calcite, Cavnic, Romania. (lower right) The "petals" of this third "flower blossom" are packed very tightly. This flower displays a single white ball sitting on a thin sphalerite matrix with a pyrite cluster on the left side. Specimen measures 6.4 cm wide and 5.6 cm high and 3.8 cm deep. Joe Budd photograph.

HEXAGONAL PRISMS

Calcite, Nikolai Mine, Dal'negorsk, Russia. (upper right) This hexagonal prism of calcite is hardly typical, since most hexagonal prisms display three-faceted, rhombohedral Mercedes-symbol terminations. This termination, features a dense, flat white cap. This single crystal measures 11.4 cm high and 6.1 cm wide. The internal fracturing and cleavage lines add a nice character to this crystal. Acquired from the Dr. Ed David collection. Joe Budd photograph.

Calcite, Sweetwater Mine, Missouri, USA. (left) Some of the most spectacular bright yellow hexagonal prisms with almost clear three-faceted Mercedes-symbol tips came from the famous Sweetwater mine in Reynolds county, Missouri. Here are a dozen sharp yellow hexagonal prisms. Specimen measures 11.4 cm high, 10.2 cm wide. The longest crystal on top is 8.9 cm. Lynn Sim photograph.

Calcite, Dachang Mine, China. (lower right) This single hexagonal prism features sharp, perfect crystals. It is also beautiful because of the spectrum of colors that reflect and refract from the internal cleavages and the prism crystal faces. There are six vertical faces, but only the front and back faces are wide. Note again the typical three-faceted rhombohedral termination. Specimen measures 10.2 cm high (long) and 6.4 cm wide. Joe Budd photograph

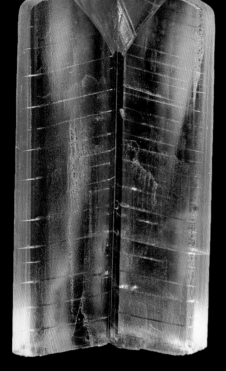

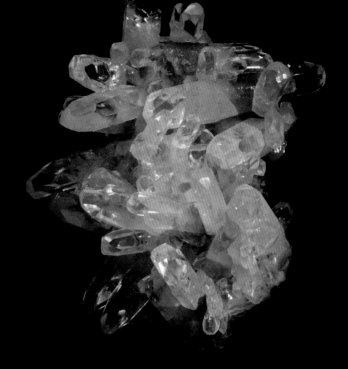

Calcite, Verschniy Mine, Dal'negorsk, Russia. This classic Calcite fishtail twin crystallography presents two twinned hexagonal prisms, sharing a common face in the center. Note the series of internal fishtail twin fracture planes moving up the entire 7.5 cm long and 3.8 cm wide crystal and the pronounced deep valley vertical twinning groove at the center top.
Lynn Sim photograph.

Calcite, Bigrigg Mine, Cumbria, England. (upper right) Bigrigg Mine is most famous for producing elongated water clear hexagonal prisms and rhombohedral terminations, sometimes with ten and even twelve facets making the tips look like cut gemstones. This piece was harvested from an early 1900's find of this pristine crystal type. Specimen measures 8.9 cm wide and 11.4 cm high. Van King photograph.

CALCITE, Charcas, Mexico. (lower left) This so-called Poker Chip calcite specimen was found several decades ago at the mines near San Luis Potosi city. The thin milky white prism is made up of the same six hexagonal prism faces, but the thinness creates a much different appearance than the rod-like prisms, When these prisms are stacked, they resemble poker chips. Specimen measures 8.9 cm x 7.5 cm, and the largest crystal is 8.3 cm across. Lynn Sim photograph.

Calcite with Amethyst and Black Hematite Selective Deposition, Artigas, Uruguay. (upper right) This unusual hexagonal prism is also-called an Angel Wing calcite because of its thinness. It was extracted from one of the basalt mines near the city of Atrigas, which borders Rio Grande do Sul, the southernmost state of Brazil. These overlapping areas are part of the world's largest lava flow region. This hexagonal prism is only 1.9 cm thick (including the front and back layers of amethyst). The center of this prism was originally white calcite, but a 1 cm to 1.2 cm wide selective deposition band of black hematite coated the outside rims of the six sides and later amethyst coated both front and back, producing this stunning pres-

entation. A fourth growth phase produced the contrasting white calcite crystals which buttress the two corners. Specimen measures 14 cm wide and 12.7 cm tall and 1.9 cm thick. Joe Budd photograph.

Calcite, Bou Azzer, Morocco. (lower right and lower left) Cobalt often provides pink colors in calcites, but these rare Moroccan calcites represent the brightest of the hot-pink colors. Specimen measures 14 cm tall by 10.2 cm wide. Jeff Scovil photographs.

Calcite on Amethyst, Irai, Brazil. This statuesque specimen poses two nearly 15.2 cm long and 3.8 cm wide hexagonal prisms sitting in a "V" pattern on a bed of amethyst quartz crystals. A real mystery about this calcite specimen is that the three rhombohedral faces seen on tip of each crystal has a deeply "engraved" vertical groove running from tip to bottom on each crystal face as if the crystals were trying to form twins but couldn't quite make it. This configuration is identical to the three deeply "engraved" black grooves on the three flat rhombohedral faces on the next calcite specimen in our gallery. The Proctors stared a long time at these two specimens separately before they made the connection between the tips of the squat, flat rhombs and these "tall" rhomb tips. This entire specimen measures 14 cm wide and 21 cm high and was found at Irai, Brazil. Joe Budd photograph.

Calcite In Amethyst Geode, Artigas, Uruguay. Most of the calcites from the basalt deposits in Brazil and Uruguay are pointed scalenohedrons, but virtually all the calcites found in Maharashtra state, India are rhombohedrons. This compact amethyst-lined basalt geode measures 25.4 cm wide, 25.4 cm deep and 30.5 cm tall. Protruding from this bed is a 10.2 cm high and 9 cm wide, fat white hexagonal calcite prism. Had miners opened this basalt geode wantonly they would have destroyed the specimen. The third growth phase selective deposition of a black iron oxide, goethite or hematite, makes up the black vertical "stripes" on the six lines defining the vertical faces. Because of their black lining, Uruguayan and Brazilian dealers and miners call these specimens "Skunks". Please see the explanation of how this selective deposition can happen in "skunks" in the *Mineralogical Record* magazine issue Vol. 40, #2 2009). There is yet a fourth growth phase. different colored small amethysts sitting on top of the "stripes" and the slightly rhombohedral hexagonal prism tip. Joe Budd photograph.

Calcite. Irai, Brazil. This 30.5 cm high and 22.9 cm wide specimen was carved from a huge basalt geode so the sceptered calcite stalks could be the focal point of the specimen. Sceptered calcite crystals are a rarity in crystals this size. The three sceptered crystals protruding from the walls range in size from 15-17 cm long and range in thickness from 2.5-5 cm, and all have perfect three-faceted rhombohedral tips, which meet and criss-cross at the center point of the geode. This, and the facing page specimen, are good examples of a matched pair and illustrate the fun and importance of collecting specimens in suites. Joe Budd photograph.

by Keith Proctor and Mauna Proctor   340

Calcite In Amethyst Vug, Irai, Brazil. There are four different growth phases represented in this magnificent crystal, because the calcite crystal is quite gemmy and also because selective hematite deposition defines different "windows" through which one can see inside the two main crystals. Specimen measures 18.4 cm high by 12.7 cm wide. Van King photograph.

Calcite Alien Mask over Amethyst. This Alien Mask, with great eyes, is a totally natural sculpture. Even the cone-shaped amethyst stalk, which bulges out where the face and eyes are, tapers to a tiny sharp point at the very top of the elongated face. Each small amethyst crystal making up the base and eyes includes sparkly black specks accentuating a darker side to the frightening demeanor. Was this face found near Roswell, New Mexico or near Irai, Brazil? Specimen measures 26.7 cm tall and 8.9 cm wide. Van King photograph.

Calcite with Hematite Inclusions, China. (upper right) This is a lovely striated multiple-growth rhombohedron with minute accents of goethite. Specimen measures 19 by 15.9 cm. Joe Budd photograph.

Calcite, Dal'negorsk Mines, Far Eastern Russia. This complex calcite crystal is only 5 cm wide by 4.4 cm high, yet it can absorb our attention for a long time as we try to figure out its crystallography. Lynn Sim photograph.

Calcite, China. (lower left) Cream-colored calcite crystals with a stacked wafer-like cluster. It appears that these crystals were trying to be true to a hexagonal prism heritage, but what could have been a prism has turned wavy with a bulge in the center, and each crystal appears to be composed of multitudes of bizarre wafer thin layers. Specimen measures 20.3 cm by 20.3 cm; the biggest crystal 12.7 cm wide. Joe Budd photograph.

Calcite, China. These are the only two specimens the Proctors saw like this. Specimen measures 16.5 cm by 11.4 cm with a 1.9 cm secondary growth calcite crystal.

Aragonite, Podrecany Mine, Western Slovenske, Rudohorie Mountains, Slovakia. Aragonite is a polymorph of calcite, which means it has the same chemical formula, but due to different temperatures and pressurest, it crystallized with a different crystal structure. Specimen measures 27.9 by 27.9 cm.
Jeff Scovil photograph.

Calcite After Ikaite in Calcite, Kola Peninsula, Russia. (lower left) A first cousin of calcite, Ikaite varies from calcite only by a single molecule of water. Ikaite is not a stable species and forms at cold temperatures. When the temperature goes above 8 degrees Celsius. ikaite's water breaks away from its chemical bonds and the residual chemicals restructure to form calcite. The sediments which may crystallize ikaite are ver rich in the principal components of calcite. The ikaite crystals are partially imbedded in calcite matrix. Specimen measures 4.4 cm x 3.8 cm x 3.2 cm. Joe Budd photograph.

Azurite, Tsumeb, Namibia. Blocky-shaped azurite crystals were found in the 1960s in only one small pocket at the renowned Tsumeb Mine. The intergrown blocky crystals show interpenetration twins. This specimen has no visible point of contact, although it has been restored. Specimen measures 8.3 cm high, 7.5 cm wide and only 5 cm thick. Joe Budd photographs.

by Keith Proctor and Mauna Proctor   346

Azurite, Milpillas, Sonora, Mexico. Great azurite crystals have been found in relatively few places, but one small occurrence at Milpillas produced many bright cobalt blue crystals. Four specimens from this rare pocket are seen pictured here, although one specimen shows both the front and reverse sides. These crystals had partially converted inside to bright green malachite, leaving only the top thin layer of azurite. These dark blue colors show some of the green malachite underneath producing a beautiful effect.
Jeff Scovil photographs.

AZURITE, Milpillas Mine, Mexico. (above left) Composition and contrast accentuate the striations in this miniature sized two crystal azurite. Specimen measures 5.7 cm wide by 3.8 cm high. (above right) Bi-colored razor-back of sharp azurite crystals. Specimen measures 7.5 cm wide by 6.4 cm high. Lynn Sim photographs.

Azurite, Guang Xi, China. (lower left) These highly textured azurite rosettes display two "flowers". 4.4 cm across. This double cluster stands 8.3 cm tall. Joe Budd photograph.

Azurite Flower Cluster Touissit, Morocco. (lower right) This radiating flower blossom measures 5 cm by 5 cm. Joe Budd photograph.

Azurite, La Sal, Utah, USA.
This old time specimen displays
four azurite "flower cluster"
rosettes on a green malachite encrusted matrix. Specimen measures 10.8 cm wide and 11.4 cm
deep and 7.5 cm thick.
Joe Budd photograph.

Azurite on Malachite, Liu Feng Shan, Anhui Province, China. (lower left and lower right) It is unusual to find azurite crystals growing on top of velvet-like malachite because azurite frequently forms first. Specimen measures 11.4 cm wide by 10.2 cm high. Joe Budd photograph.

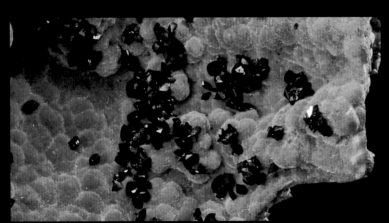

Azurite, La Sal, Utah, USA. This 7.5 cm wide by 5.7 cm high flower cluster rosette is among the largest found at the mine. Note the brown limonite matrix impregnated with green feathery malachite buds. The big azurite rosette itself has minute spots of green malachite. Joe Budd photograph.

Malachite Pseudo-morph After Azurite, on Cobaltoan Calcite, Bou Azzer, Morocco. The outrageous color combination makes this 6.4 cm wide and 5 cm tall green malachite specimen proclaim "Color Is King!" Joe Budd photograph

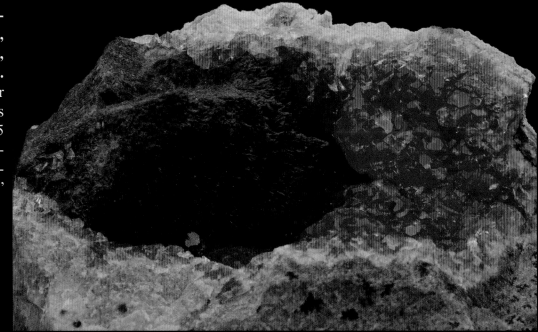

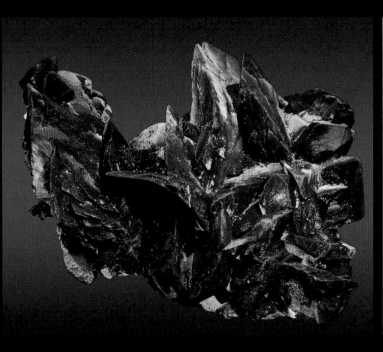

 Malachite Pseudomorph After Azurite, Milpillas Mine, Sonora, Mexico. (lower left and lower right) This great azurite pseudomorphed to malachite, and its colorful velvet sheen is captivating. It is impossible to capture the beauty of this specimen with one photo because as one moves the piece, flashes of electric green seem to move across the surface. Specimen measures 12.7 cm wide by 10.2 cm tall.
Lower left view - Van King photograph. Lower right view - Lynn Sim photograph.

Malachite, Star Of The Congo Mine, Congo. These sparkly dark green primary malachite botryoids are exceptional. The matrix is sparkly red limonite permeated with quartz. Complimentary colors along with the proper size ratio between the crystals and matrix are two of the most important criteria determining specimen beauty and investment value. Specimen measures 6.4 cm wide and 8.9 cm high. Joe Budd photograph.

by Keith Proctor and Mauna Proctor   352

Malachite, Kolwezi, Congo. (upper left) Here is a 12 cm wide, by 12.7 cm wide botryoidal malachite with two different colors. The dark color is due to iron in the mineral. Two remarkable 11.4 cm tall flume chimneys project out of the center. The Proctors acquired this specimen personally from a mineral dealer in Guiling, China. Joe Budd photograph.

Malachite, Katanga, Congo. (lower left and lower right) This is a bi-color flume chimney of malachite. Such a formation is only possible in an open cavity. Specimen measures 12.7 cm wide by 8.9 cm deep and chimney is 14 cm tall. Lynn Sim photographs.

Malachite, Star Of Congo Mine Congo. These malachite spheres were formed near the Earth's surface. Specimen measures 5 cm wide and 3.8 cm high.
Joe Budd photograph.

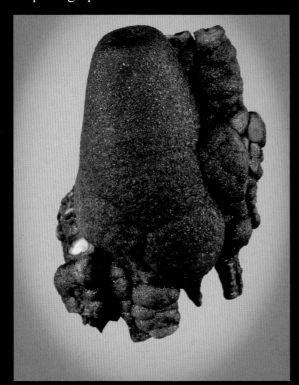

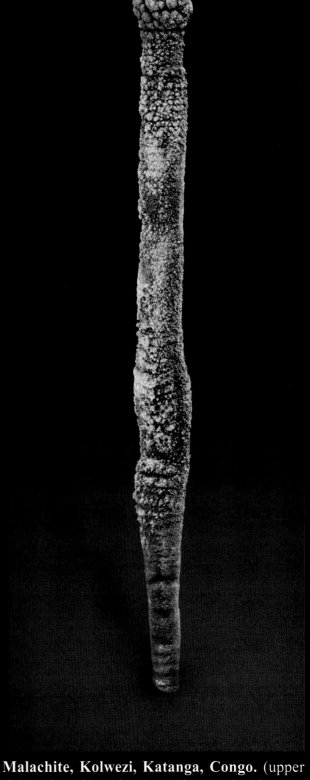

Malachite, Katanga, Congo. (lower left) A conical malachite showing a velvety surface and elongated flume chimneys. 10.2 cm tall. Lynn Sim photograph.

Malachite, Kolwezi, Katanga, Congo. (upper right) Viewed here is 26.7 cm long malachite "stalactite" that is 2.5 cm wide at its widest.
Joe Budd photograph.

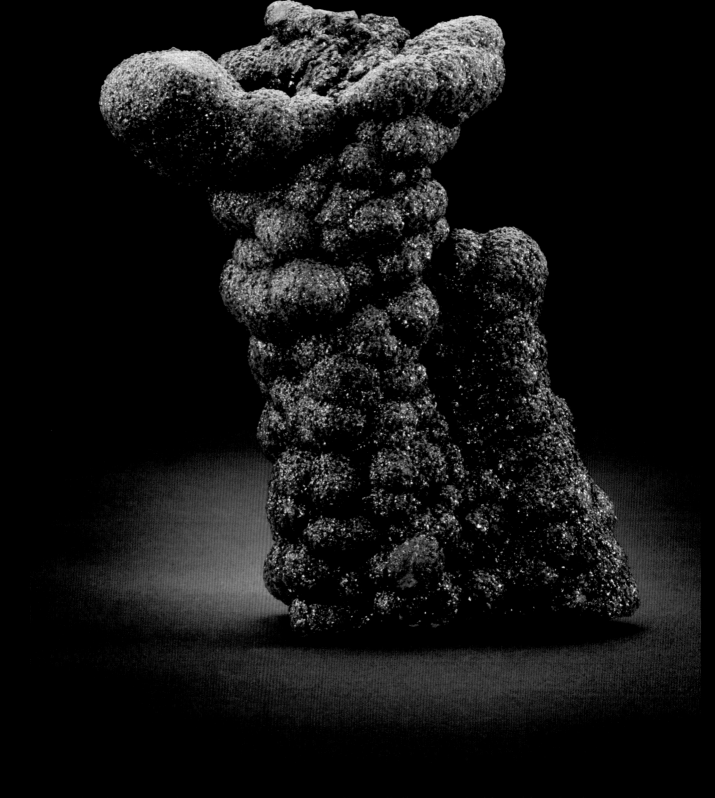

Malachite, Katanga, Congo. Here we see an excellent tall display malachite with stalactite growth. 12.5 cm tall. Joe Budd photograph.

355 *The Keith and Mauna Proctor Collection*

Malachite And Azurite, Sea Bra, Bahia State, Brazil. Azurite "caught in the act" of alteration to malachite. Specimen measures 6.4 cm wide by 5 cm high.

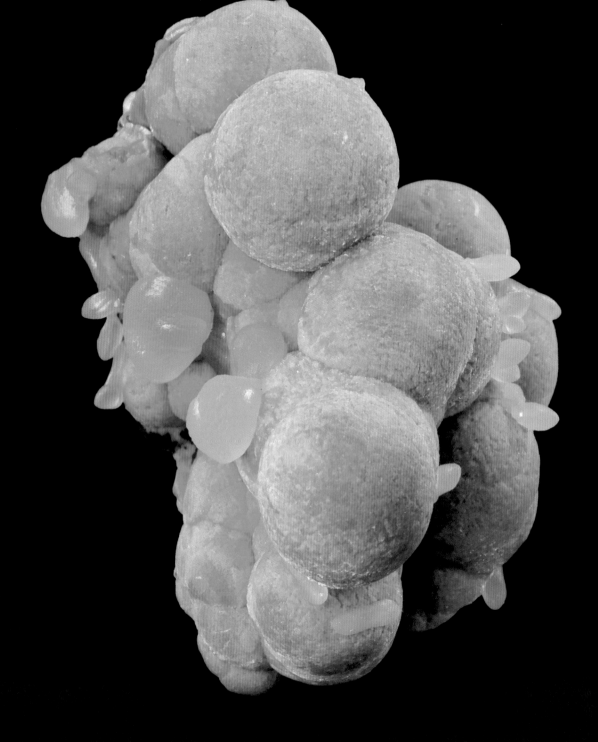

Smithsonite on Aurichalcite, Kelly Mine, Magdalena, New Mexico, USA. This specimen measures 4 cm long by 3.2 cm wide, and exhibits both brilliant and shiny botryoidal aurichalcite as well as small blue-green crystals of smithsonite colored by inclusions of aurichalcite. Joe Budd photograph.

Smithsonite, Rodeo Mine, Choix, Sinola, Mexico. This 8.9 cm wide by 7.5 cm high hot pink, botryoidal Smithsonite is colored by cobalt. Joe Budd photograph.

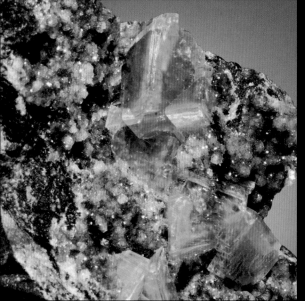

Smithsonite, Tsumeb Mine, Namibia. The exciting green color in this smithsonite comes from a rich concentration of copper atoms as an impurity, and the individual 1.3 cm crystals are uncommonly large for the species. Specimen measures 7 cm high by 5 cm wide. Joe Budd photograph.

Smithsonite, Kelly Mine, Magdalena, New Mexico, USA. (above right) Delicate baby blue smithsonite crystals in globular clusters on limonite matrix. 5 cm wide. Lynn Sim photograph.

Smithsonite, El Rugio Mine, Choix, Sinaloa, Mexico. (upper right) Three distinct colors of smithsonite appear on this specimen. The main (part of the specimen is rich neon blue. A later white growth layer flows from the top and is finally frosted by orange smithsonite, colored by iron staining. Each layer accentuates the others and adds to the appeal. Specimen measures 5.7 cm by 7 cm. Joe Budd photograph.

Smithsonite, Tsumeb Mine, Namibia. Glassy crystals of cream-colored smithsonite featuring dozens of sharp, semitransparent crystals forming a gentle cleft. Light dances on their faces. The rhombohedral crystal shape is sharp for the species. Ex. Matthew Webb specimen. Specimen measures 7.5 cm by 8.9 cm. Joe Budd photograph.

Smithsonite, Tsumeb Mine, Namibia. (lower right) Pale pink rhombohedrons of smithsonite on dolomite. Specimen measures 5.7 cm by 6.1 cm.
Joe Budd photograph.

Smithsonite After Sphalerite Crystals, Philadelphia Mine, Rush, Marion County, Arkansas, USA. (upper right) Bright yellow crystals of rice-grain-shaped smithsonites are pseudomorphed as well as overlaying this entire specimen. Specimen is 13.2 cm by 9.5 cm. Joe Budd photograph.

Smithsonite Pseudomorph After Dolomite, Philadelphia Mine, Rush, Arkansas, USA. (below) This exciting pseudomorph shows the saddleback structure of the original dolomite. The yellow color in Philadelphia Mine smithsonites comes from inclusions of greenockite. These Arkansas smithsonites were found about 1995. Specimen is 7 cm by 12.7 cm. Joe Budd photograph.

Rhodochrosite on Quartz, Blue Moon Pocket, Sweet Home Mine, Alma, Colorado, USA. Because of its red color and glassy faces, rhodochrosite is undoubtedly one of the most popular minerals in the world, competing with native gold, tourmaline, emerald, and aquamarine. This 10.2 cm rhombohedral crystal of gemmy rhodochrosite is accentuated by its spectacular needle-like white quartz crystals. Some of the quartzes actually penetrate the rhodochrosite rhomb. Interspersed among the quartz crystals are the uncommon mineral tetrahedrite along with crystals of pyrite and sphalerite. Specimen measures 22.9 cm by 19.7 cm.
Joe Budd photograph.

Rhodochrosite, N'Chwaning II Mine, Kuruman, South Africa. These brilliant red pointed scalenohedral clusters from the N'Chwaning mine were found several decades ago. Everyone expected there would be more, but the supply soon was finished. The richness of color, the high luster, and the gemminess of these rhodochrosites are now part of legend, although the mine is enormous and is still working at this writing. Specimen measures 8.9 cm x 8.9 cm. Joe Budd photograph.

363   *The Keith and Mauna Proctor Collection*

Siderite Pseudomorph After Calcite, Turt Mine, Oas Satu Mare, Romania. (upper right) These bizarre siderite rhombohedron crystals reflect the shape of the long gone calcite underneath, but add an overhang on each crystal. Specimen measures 10.2 cm by 8.9 cm and the largest crystal is 3.2 cm. Joe Budd photograph.

Siderite, The Rist Mine, North Carolina, USA. Books of black Biotite Mica compliment these complete and shiny rhombohedrons of siderite. This miniature-sized (5 cm by 5 cm) cluster is five intergrown, brownish green rhombohedrons of siderite. This specimen was acquired from the Dr. Ed David collection. Joe Budd photograph.

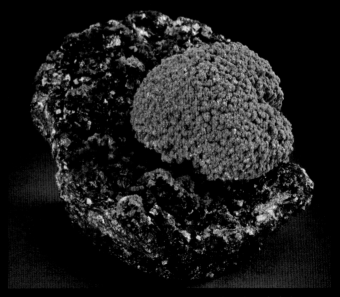

Siderite Pseudomorph After Calcite, Turt Mine, Romania. (lower left) This huge 7 cm rhombohedron of siderite sits on a 7.5 cm high by 8.3 cm wide siderite matrix. Joe Budd photograph.

Siderite, Turt Mine, Romania. (lower right) Here we see a very reddish brown sphere of siderite sitting on pyrite crystals. This is a rare habit for siderite. The sphere is 3.8 cm across and the specimen overall measures 7.5 cm wide, and 8.3 cm deep.
Joe Budd photograph.

by Keith Proctor and Mauna Proctor   364

Cerussite Snowflake Crystals, Tsumeb, Nambia.
(above left) Snowflake crystal cluster of complicated, intergrown, and branched V-twin crystals. Specimen is 9.5 cm wide and 10.2 cm tall. Lynn Sim photograph.

Cerussite, Kombat Mine, Namibia. (above right) These twinned gem crystals of cerussite refract light in a rainbow spectrum of colors just as leaded crystal does. Specimen is 3.2 cm. Joe Budd photograph.

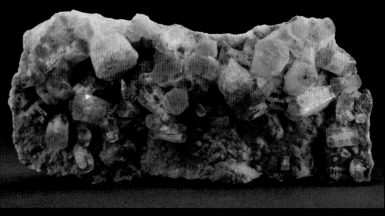

Strontianite, Oberdorf, Austria. (right) This is an excellent strontianite specimen and has golden brown, barrel-shaped crystals on a matrix. 15.2 cm wide and 7.5 cm tall, with almost 2.5 cm long crystals. This species is virtually unobtainable in the market. Keith traveled 100 miles north of Vienna to Oberdorf to acquire this specimen from an oldtime collection. Joe Budd photograph.

Cerussite,Tsumeb Mine, Namibia. (lower left) Another crystal habit in cerussite is the sixling twin, which consists of three V-twins arranged in a cycle or wheel-ike pattern. 3.2 cm high. Joe Budd photograph.

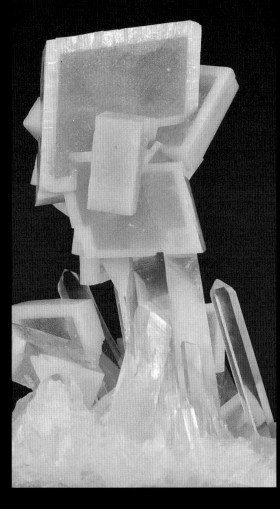

Barite on Calcite, Elk Creek, South Dakota, USA. (lower right) Elk Creek barites are found in hardened mud, but have been a benchmark for color and quality for many years. This specimen is 8.9 cm high and 8.9 cm wide and the dark amber crystal is 7 cm long. Jeff Scovil photograph.

by Keith Proctor and Mauna Proctor   366

Barite, Parkside Mine, Cumbria, England. (upper left) This cluster of three crystals measures 3.8 cm wide, 8.3 cm high and was probably mined near the turn of the nineteenth century. Joe Budd photograph.

Barite, China. (upper right) The phantoms in this barite indicate that it grew in stages/layers. Specimen measures 8.9 cm by 7.5 cm. Joe Budd photograph.

Barite, Autun, France. (lower left) Great surface markings and phantoms are the hallmark of this cluster of nearly 40 stave-shaped yellow barite crystals. Specimen measures 7.5 cm by 8.9 cm. Joe Budd photograph.

Barite, Huarancaca, Peru. (lower right) This natural-colored Barite shows what a "pure" barite would look like. Specimen measures 7.5 cm tall (including the matrix) by 6.4 cm wide. Lynn Sim photograph.

Barite, Meickle Mine, Nevada.
(right) A Nevada gold mine produced choice yellow gem tabular
barites associated with calcite.
Specimen measures 14.6 cm by 7.5
cm wide. Joe Budd photograph.

**Barite, Ganzhou Prefecture,
Jiangxi Province, China.** (left)
The unexpected intersecting angles
bring dramatic visual tension to this
basically colorless barite. Specimen
measures 8.9 cm tall by 7.5 cm
wide. Van King photograph.

by Keith Proctor and Mauna Proctor   368

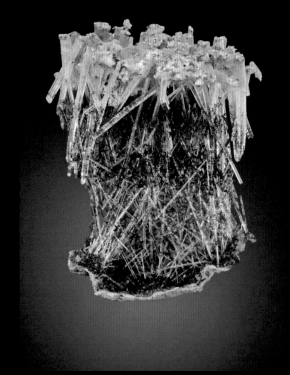

Gypsum, Lubin, Poland. (upper right) A sulfur mine produced gypsum crystals of three colors sitting on an extremely thin bowl shaped matrix. Specimen measures 4 tall and 7 cm across. Joe Budd photograph

Gypsum – Rams Horn Selenite, Morocco: (upper left) Seen here is an artistic "Rams Horn" gypsum with curly crystals which has been "extruded" from a small (7.5 cm wide) piece of matrix. Specimen is 12.7 cm tall and 11.4 cm wide. Joe Budd photograph.

Gypsum, Lilly Mine, Ica, Peru. (lower right) Specimen measures 7.5 cm wide and 8.9 cm tall with the longe gem crystal measuring 6.4 cm tall. Joe Budd photograph

Gypsum, Red River Floodway, Manitoba, Canada, (upper right) This interesting specimen probably formed as an evaporation product in a sandy deposit. Specimen measures 6.4 cm wide by 6.4 cm tall. Van King photograph.

Gypsum Fish Tail Twin, Naica, Mexico: (upper left) Specimen measure 14 cm tall by 8.9 cm wide. Van King photograph.

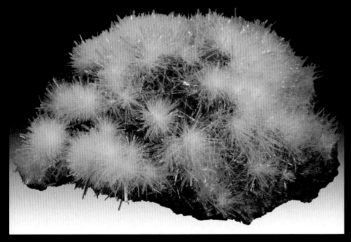

"Chrysanthemum Flower" – Gypsum Imprint On Slate. (lower right) Specimen measures 8.9 cm. Joe Budd photograph.

Gypsum. (lower left) Starbursts of delicate Gypsum Crystals. Specimen measures 15.2 cm wide. Lynn Sim photograph.

Anglesite, Touissit, Morocco. Gemmy yellow anglesite crystals on a 5 cm tall by 3.8 cm wide matrix. Joe Budd photograph.

Celestine with Sulphur, Wroclaw, Poland. (upper left) Bursting from the top of yellow sulfur crystals is a beautiful cluster of very gemmy blue Celestine crystals (a strontium sulfate species). Wroclaw, Poland sulfur mines. Specimen measures 12.7 cm wide.
Joe Budd photograph

Celestine With Fluorite, Musquez, Mexico. (upper right) This statuesque white Celestine group has a purple fluorite crystal perched on one corner. Specimen measures 1.3 cm wide and 8.9 cm tall.
Joe Budd photograph.

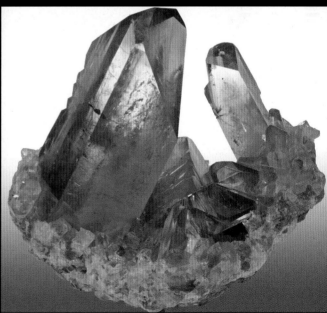

Anglesite, Touissit, Morocco. (lower left) Here we see four, small yellow gemmy anglesite crystals sitting on a galena matrix. Specimen measures 3.8 cm wide and 2.5 cm tall.
Joe Budd photograph.

Celestine, Mahajanga Mine, Majunga Province, Madagascar. (lower right) In 1798 Celestine was so named because of its pale sky-blue color. Many fine gem crystals have come from the island of Madagascar. Crystal measures 8.9 cm. Jeff Scovil photograph.

by Keith Proctor and Mauna Proctor   372

Creedite, Navidad Mine, Mexico. (upper view) Beautiful bright orange creedite crystal specimens were found in Mexico nearly ten years ago. This discovery produced brilliant orange crystals as beautiful and popular as the pale lavender colored crystals found at Santa Eulalia, Mexico decades ago. Because of its form, color, and rarity the specimens were quickly gobbled up, virtually disappearing into the market. There are more than 100 bright orange crystals here (some 1.3 cm long). This stunning double sphere group measures 10.2 cm wide and 6.4 cm high. Van King photograph.

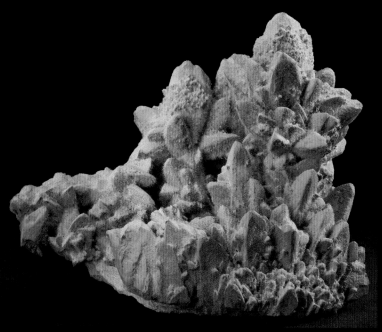

Posnjakite - Langite, France. (lower left) Seen here is certainly one of the rarest and most colorful pseudomorph species. From a one-time small find this is a brilliant and very sculptural, turquoise colored cluster of calcite crystals replaced by posnjakite and langite. Specimen measures 11.4 cm wide and 11.4 cm tall.
Joe Budd photograph.

Arsenates

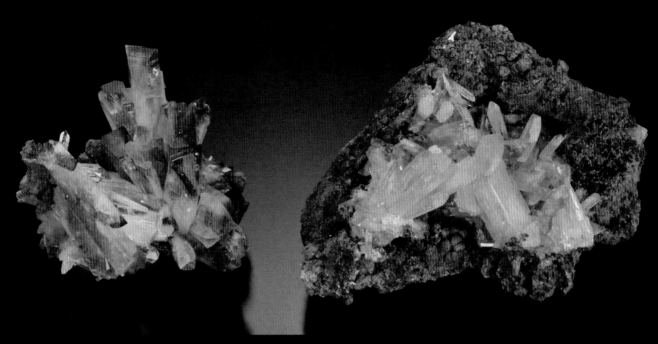

Adamite and Legrandite, Ojuela Mine, Mapimi, Durango, Mexico. The is a duo of pretty minerals from the same location. Adamite crystals (upper left) are generally thought to be yellow of green, but the huge purple adamites were a sensation when they were first found. The purple tips on the white adamite are gorgeous. These manganese-rich adamite crystals harvested in 1982 feature bright purple tips. There were only a few pockets and certainly too few specimens for the whole world market. Most legrandite crystals (upper right) are miniscule, but some good gemmy crystal groups of bright yellow legrandite were found. The adamite is about 3 x 3 cm, while the legrandite is about 5 x 6 cm. Joe Budd photograph.

Adamite, Ojuela Mine, Mexico. (lower left) This classic example represents the standard color and texture most commonly seen in adamite. Specimen measures 7.5 cm by 6.4 cm. Lynn Sim photograph

Adamite, Ojuela Mine-Mapimi, Durango, Mexico. (lower right) These copper-rich adamite crystals were acquired from a German collection. These isolated crystals on their contrasting matrix are attractive. Specimen measures 12.7 cm tall by 8.9 cm wide. Joe Budd photograph.

by Keith Proctor and Mauna Proctor   374

Mimetite, Pingtouling mine, Quingyan Prefecture, Guangdong Province, China. (upper left) This minia-ture sized specimen displays two different crystal shapes. This piece was pictured in *Fine Minerals of China,* Dr. Liu's definitive book on Chinese minerals. Specimen measures 5 cm high and 3.8 cm high.
Joe Budd photograph.

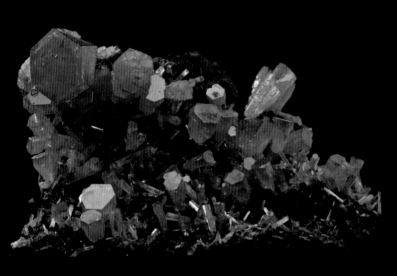

Mimetite.Pingtouling Mine, Quingyan Prefecture, Guang-dong Province, China. (center left) Arsenate species are top priority collector items because of their distinct colors and de-lightful crystallography. Note the internal glow in these in-tensely colored, six-sided mimetite crystals.
Joe Budd photograph.

Mimetite, Pingtouling Mine, China. (upper right) This miniature-sized specimen displays a huge 2.5 cm crystal. Jeff Scovil photograph.

MIMETITE, **Aleura Mine Australia.** (lower left) The Aleura mine produced a few bright yellow-green crystal specimens. Specimen measures 6.4 cm x 6.4 cm.
Lynn Sim photograph.

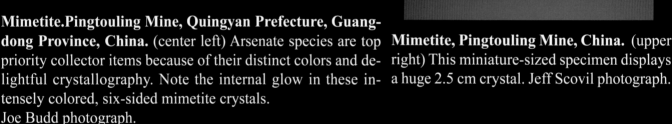

Vanadinite, Mibladen, Morocco. (above right) 5 cm x 6.4 cm: Same glassy faces and translucent rims as above left, but slightly smaller crystals. Joe Budd photograph.

Vanadinite on white bladed Barite, Mibladen, Morocco. (above left) 11.4 cm by 7.5 cm with gemmy 1.6 cm crystals. Joe Budd photograph.

Vanadinite, Touissit, Morocco. (lower right) Shiny arsenic-rich crystals completely cover "The Ram's Head". Touissit had a few areas rich in arsenic, which produced this unique cream color instead of the red color typical of Mibladen. Specimen measures 11.4 cm x 7.5 cm. Joe Budd photograph.

Descloizite, Berg Aukus Mine, Near Grootfontain, Namibia. (upper left) Large single crystal. Its shape is due to rapid dendritic growth not unlike frost on a window. Specimen measures 6.4 cm tall by 5 cm wide. Lynn Sim photograph.

Pyromorphite, Bunker Hill Mine, Kellogg, Idaho, USA. (lower left) Only one pocket producing a handful of specimens of this rare color of pyromorphite was discovered at the Bunker Hill mine. Specimen measures: 7 cm tall.
Joe Budd photograph.

Pyromorphite, Bunker Hill Mine, Kellogg, Idaho, USA. (right) Pyromorphite, perched on a reddish limonite matrix, demonstrates the artistic quality connoisseur collectors try to acquire. Specimen measures 7 cm tall. Longest crystal is 2.5 cm.
Joe Budd photograph.

Pyromorphite, Daoping Mine, China. (above) Cylindrical, hexagonal prisms present a luscious green color with brilliant shiny faces. Specimen measures 7 cm. Joe Budd photograph.

(below) **Pyromorphite, Daoping Mine, China.** (lower left) Green, cylindrical and fan shaped crystals. Specimen measures 7 cm wide. Joe Budd photograph.

Pyromorphite, Les Farges Mine, France. (upper right)
The hollow "hoppered" crystals on this specimen measuring 7 cm high probably indicate a quick growth rate. Joe Budd photograph.

Pyromorphite, Bunker Hill Mine, Kellogg, Idaho, USA. (upper left) Bunker Hill Mine also produced these wonderful globular crystals in clusters reminding one of the mimetite variety called campylite. Specimen measures 7 cm wide and 5 cm high. Jeff Scovil photograph.

Pyromorphite,: Bunker Hill Mine, Kellogg, Idaho, USA. (lower left) Specimen measures 7.5 cm tall. Lynn Sim photograph.

Pyromorphite, Bunker Hill Mine, Kellogg, Idaho, USA. (upper left) This masterpiece specimen exhibits a multitude of bi-color crystals olive green on the bottom with yellow tips. The matrix of this specimen is very thin, and when turned over one sees that the matrix was the top of a hardened molten bubble. It was a miracle that this specimen survived. Specimen measures 8.9 cm.
Lynn Sim photograph

Pyromorphite, Bunker Hill Mine, Kellogg, Idaho, USA. (upper right) The Proctor's decided years ago to collect similarly sized pyromorphite specimens. This suite is a classic example of the synergism and dramatic appeal available when one places several high quality similar-sized examples together for study. Miniature size specimens are almost always the more perfect and easier to match. Specimen measures: 7 cm high. Joe Budd photograph.

Pyromorphite, Bunker Hill Mine, Kellogg, Idaho, USA. (lower left) Specimen measures 4.4 cm across. Joe Budd photograph.

Apatite, Nagar Valley, Pakistan. (upper right) Apatite is a phosphate species. One of the popular colors is the pink type from Pakistan. The crystal seen here is 5 cm tall. The bottom half of this crystal is very gemmy. Specimen measures: 10.8 cm wide and 7.5 cm tall. This is a slightly restored specimen. Joe Budd photograph.

Apatite, Panasqueira, Portugal. (center right) The best green color apatites came from Panasqueira. This one has good gemminess, hexagonal-shaped crystals with dark centers, and attractive beveled edges. Specimen measures 7.5 cm wide. Joe Budd photograph.

Apatite, Cerro De Mercado, Durango, Mexico. (upper left) We view here a superb yellow gem crystal of apatite with a hexagonal tip. Specimen measures 3.8 cm high. Joe Budd photograph.

Apatite, Nuristan, Afghanistan. (lower left) Some of the least common apatites exhibit the lavender to purple colors. This specimen unusually elongated for lavender apatite. Specimen measures 6.4 cm high. Joe Budd photograph

Vivianite, Huanuni, Bolivia. (upper right) Another most popular phosphate species is vivianite which rarely occurs in huge gemmy green crystals as seen here. This beautiful specimen measures: 12.7 cm tall and the main gemmy doubly terminated crystal 8.3 cm long. This specimen was acquired on trade from Dr. Steve Neely in Tennessee. Jeff Scovil photograph.

Brazilianite, Linopolis, M.G., Brazil. (lower right) We see here another very popular phosphate species rarely found in big crystals. Large crystals have been found in only three small deposits since mid-1940s - all in Brazil. Specimen measures 7.5 cm by 5.7 cm.
Joe Budd photograph.

Montebrasite, Linopolis, Minas Gerais, Brazil. Reputed by both Brian Lees and Steve Behling to be by far the best specimen of this species. From the gem pegmatite mines of Brazil. This is phosphate rarely comes in crystals, but for a few localities. These two pale yellow crystals in a "V" pattern are quite gemmy in areas. This specimen has been slightly restored.
Jeff Scovil photograph.

Wulfenite, Rowley Mine, Theba, Arizona. (both views) This pocket of delicate bright orange wulfenites from the famed Rowley Mine is a singular occurrence because of the multitude of gemmy crystals. This mine produced very few good specimens such as this one.

Joe Budd photographs.

Wulfenite, Santa Eulalia, Mexico. (upper left) The Santa Eulalia mines seldom produced any wulfenite specimens, but years ago Peter McGaw brought a few of these rare yellow groups from Mexico. This color is extremely bright for any wulfenite locality. This specimen is 5.7 cm high. Joe Budd photograph.

Wulfenite, Red Cloud Mine, Arizona, USA. (above right and lower left) Two classic wulfenite examples illustrate that miniature-sized specimens are often more perfect than larger specimens and usually gemmier. The specimen above measures 2.5 cm tall. Joe Budd photograph.

Wulfenite, Red Cloud Mine, Arizona, USA. (lower left) This miniature intensely colored wulfenite is a joy to behold. It has color, smooth and lustrous faces, transparency, and aesthetic proportions. Specimen measures 5 cm high. Joe Budd photograph.

(right) **Wulfenite, Red Cloud Mine, Arizona.** (upper right) Perfect crystal dispersal and bold color make this a visually stunning specimen. The proportionately sized thin matrix is also a plus. Specimen measures 6.4 cm wide by 3.8 cm high. Jeff Scovil photograph.

Wulfenite, Ojuela Mine, Mapimi, Durango, Mexico. (lower left) A great discovery of rare crystals with two alternating shape types occurred in a small discovery at Ojuela (midnight) mine, Mapimi, Mexico. Pictured here is an enlargement of part of the whole specimen which measures 15.2 cm by 15 cm. Jeff Scovil photograph.

Wulfenite, Los Lamentos Mine, Mexico. (lower right) The largest huge crystal seen here is almost 3.8 cm across. Specimen measures: 10.8 cm tall and 6.4 cm wide.
Joe Budd photograph.

by Keith Proctor and Mauna Proctor   386

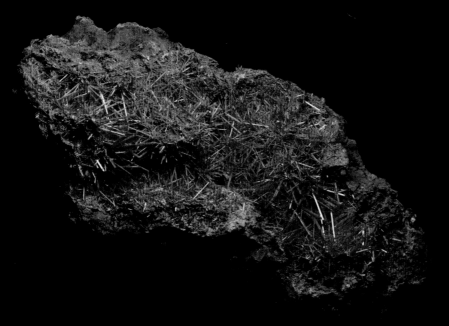

Crocoite, Adelaide Mine, Dundas, Tasmania. (upper left and lower left) The extremely bright crystals above and left comprise one of the great crocoite specimens mined circa 1973. Specimen measures 25.4 cm x 12.5 cm. Van King photograph.

Crocoite, Red Lead Mine, Dundas, Tasmania. (lower right) This is a large, terminated single crystal. Specimen measures 8.9 cm x 0.6 cm. Joe Budd photograph.

Tungstates

Scheelite, Mount Xuebaoding, Ping Wu County, Sichaun Province, China. (upper right) This species is tetragonal in crystal habit, and thus produces pseudo octahedral crystals. Orange is not a common color at all and a large crystal showing this intensity of color is remarkable. Specimen is 6.4 cm tall x 7.5 cm wide. Lynn Sim photograph.

Ferberite, Mundo Nuevo (New Moon) Mine At La Libertad, Peru. (upper left) Precise crystallography and color contrasting textured clear quartz matrix make this a perfect specimen. 22.9 cm x 11.4 cm. This specimen is illustrated as a front cover photo on the September 2000 issue of *Mineralogical Record* magazine. Jeff Scovil photograph.

Scheelite, Xuebaoding Mountain, China. (lower left) Few scheelite crystals are gemmy, especially if big, but this is a transparent 2.5 cm wide gem crystal sitting on a 7.5 cm wide matrix. Joe Budd photograph.

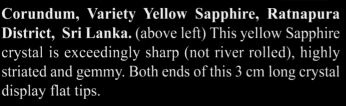

Corundum, Variety Yellow Sapphire, Ratnapura District, Sri Lanka. (above left) This yellow Sapphire crystal is exceedingly sharp (not river rolled), highly striated and gemmy. Both ends of this 3 cm long crystal display flat tips.

Corundum, Variety Ruby, Jegdalek, Afghanistan. (above right) We view here two fine ruby crystal specimen s- each on a marble matrix. The one on the right is exceptional because of its unusual translucency. The crystal on the left is mostly opaque but it shows better crystal striations. The larger ruby is 3 cm tall.
Lynn Sim photographs.

Corundum, Variety Blue Sapphire, Ratnapura District, Sri Lanka. (lower right) Sapphire is a gem species and along with ruby – is a most famous oxide species. With collectors and jewelry buffs, the two most popular colors to collect are blue and yellow. This superb 5.7 cm long light blue crystal is highly striated (not river rolled), and has slightly flat terminations at both ends.

Spinel On Calcite, Luc Yen, Vietnam. Spinel is the second most popular oxide species (after sapphire) used in the jewelry trade. Ruby spinel is rarely found in large gemmy crystals, and most used for cut stones are found in the gem gravels of Myan Mar. It is rare to find large sharp and gemmy crystals. Along with occasional highly distorted and opaque ruby crystals, Luc Yen also produced large spinel-twinned crystals of ruby spinel. The Proctors acquired this choice 3 cm by 2.5 cm spinel-twinned crystal on color contrasting white marble matrix through their Vietnam contact. This magnificent display specimen measures 8.9 cm wide and 7.5 cm tall, and the red crystal is a huge, textbook-perfect 3 cm tall spinel twin. View B (above right) shows the twinning plane.
view A photograph by Joe Budd.
view B photograph by Lynn Sim.

Chrysoberyl, Ambamdapondrazaka, Alaotra-Mangoro Region, Madagascar. It is unusual to find a V-twin chrysoberyl on the same specimen with a sixling twin. The bigger flat crystal flaunts surface radiating lines that clearly demonstrating that this is a sixling twin; the points just didn't separate into six divisions as do cerussite twins. Specimen measures 0.6 cm by 3.8 cm. Lynn Sim photograph.

Cassiterite on Muscovite Mica, Mount Xuebaoding, Ping Wu County, China. (upper right) This highly textured twinned (8.9 cm long) cassiterite crystal, from this classic, scheelite and cassiterite deposit, is encrusted by white muscovite mica crystals. Joe Budd photograph.

Cassiterite, Mt. Xuebaoding, Sichuan Province, China. (lower right) Seen here is a twinned, bi-pyramidal cassiterite crystal measuring 5 cm by 6.4 cm. Joe Budd photograph.

Rutile, Novo Horizonte, Bahia, Brazil. (upper left and upper right) This elegant specimen has a flat, black, disk-shaped hematite crystal with many golden rutile needles radiating from its edges in a starburst spray. These golden needles are also sprinkled liberally over the quartz-covered matrix. The center hematite crystals seen here in photographs A and B acted as a template for the growth of the delicate golden rutile needles. This specimen is 15.2 cm tall and 12.7 cm wide. Joe Budd photograph.

Brookite On Quartz, Baluchistan, Pakistan. (lower right) Brookite is trimorphous with rutile and anatase (all three have identical formulas but different shapes). This world-class example found at Pakistan measures 6.4 cm wide by 6.4 cm tall; its main brown-red, flat gem crystal is 3.8 cm tall. This is huge for the species. Joe Budd photograph.

Hematite Iron Roses (Eisen Roses, Tessen, Switzerland. Seen here is an interesting "Iron Rose" specimen which was dug in the 1960s by a Swiss strahler (an alpine rock climber and digger). It has a half dozen shiny Iron Roses in a cluster. The biggest "rose" on top is 2.5 cm across. If we turn this specimen around we find (upper left) a very narrow black line from the bottom of the matrix up the backside leading to the topmost a crack in the rock to form this cluster of "iron roses".
Upper left view A photo by Van King. Upper right view B photo by Jeff Scovil.

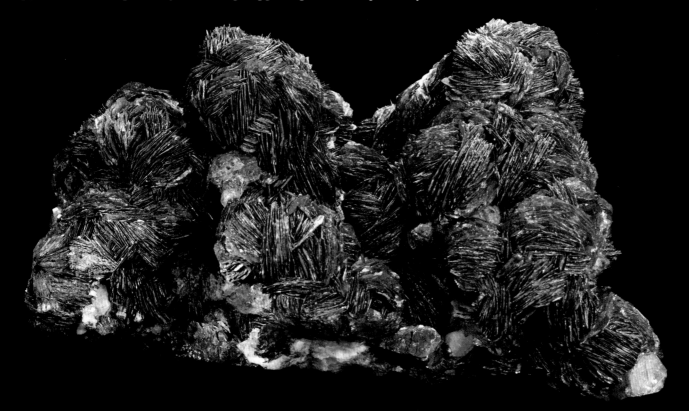

Hematite, Jinlong Mine, China. (lower view) This is a tightly knit specimen of black hematite rosettes. Specimen measures 12.7 cm by 6.4 cm. Van King photograph.

(right) Hematite With Rutile Crystals, Cavaradi, Switzerland. (upper right) The rutile association is characteristic of specimens such as these comes from Cavaradi, Switzerland. Specimen measures 4.4 cm by 4.4 cm. Lynn Sim photograph.

Hematite Pseudomorphs After Marcasite, White Desert, Libya. (center) This group of three marcasite specimens – all measuring 3.8 cm to 5 cm across, are pseudomorphed to hematite. Two of the pieces look like jacks from the old-time kid's game.
Joe Budd photograph.

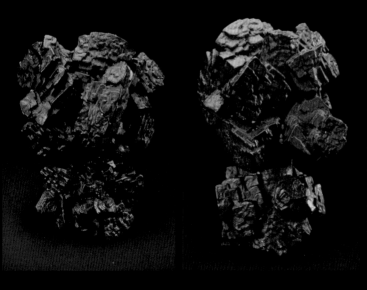

Hematite Pseudomorph After Pyrite, White Desert, Libya. (two lower left) These sculptural hematite after pyrite pseudomorphs from the White Desert are quite different from the pseudomorphs after marcasite in that all the crystals formed around a central "tube" that can be seen in view B. We know these are pyrites instead of marcasites because these crystals are definitely cubic shape. Pyrite, with the same formula, is a polymorph of Marcasite. Specimen measures 5.7 cm high by 3.8 cm wide. Joe Budd photographs.

Goethite/Limonite, China. (upper right) This multi-colored iron oxide mineral specimen is made of iron oxides, as is hematite. Usually, goethite occurs as unattractive black, brown/black, or reddish colors, but this specimen is attractive as two bronze-green iridescent "under sea cannons" lie one on top of the other. This iridescent luster is probably from oxidation on the surface. This specimen measures 14.6 cm long and 5.7 cm high. Joe Budd photograph.

Betafite, Silver Crater Mine, Wilberforce, Ontario, Canada. (lower left) Betafite is a rare uranium, niobium, titanium species. This specimen displays a classic fourteen-sided cubo-octahedral crystal (isometric system). Specimen measures 3.8 cm wide by 3 cm tall. Joe Budd photograph.

Magnetite and Hematite Pseudomorphs After Magnetite, Payun Volcano, Mendoza Province, Argentina. Hematite and magnetite are both iron oxides. The original "miners" thought these were hematite specimens, so they were immensely puzzled by this octahedral shape. The pseudomorphs have varying degrees of completeness. In the specimen on the left, the surfaces of these modified octahedrons are mostly free of hematite and are strongly magnetitic. The other two specimens are extensively replaced by hematite and their magnetism is much diminished. Magnetite has an important biological value. Most migrating animals, as well as Monarch butterflies, use specks of Magnetite in their bodies to navigate their way "home". These intriguingly stacked octahedrons exhibit dramatic tension; they might topple over at any moment. The points display aesthetic balance and restate the geometric precision retained during their growth and final crystallization. Some of these stacked octahedrons display a rougher finish than the first, because they are totally altered on their surfaces to hematite. Again, their stacked and balanced presentation has a focal point and a tension which draws and holds our attention. (lower left) 8.9 cm high by 7 cm. Joe Budd photograph. (above left) 8.3 cm high. Jeff Scovil photograph. (upper right)10.2 cm high. Jeff Scovil photograph.

Realgar, Cavnic, Romania: (above left) This 6.4 cm x 5.7 cm quartz matrix covered with eight large Realgar crystals (which are a much different shape than those on the previous specimen) is from a very small find in Romania. Most crystals are doubly terminated and 0.6 cm thick and 3.2 cm long.
Joe Budd photograph.

Cinnabar, Yunchanping Mine, Tongren District, Guizhou Province, China. (lower left) Seen here is a red to white color-contrasting plate of gemmy red Cinnabar crystals sprinkled over brilliant white Dolomite crystals. These crystals are not twinned as some Cinnabar crystals are. Specimen measures 9.5 cm high and 6.4 cm wide. Joe Budd photograph.

Realgar, Shimen Arsenic Mine, China. (lower right) Displayed here is one of the best Realgar crystals found at the Shimen Arsenic Mine. This brilliant gem crystal, acquired from the Dr. Steve Neely collection is 8.9 cm tall and 3.2 cm wide. Only a few of these completely gem crystals were ever found. The longest crystal of all – twice as long as this one – was accidently dropped and completely destroyed by a Chinese dealer. Note: *all realgar specimens* are unstable in bright lights and will quickly start to convert to dusty parealgar. This is a restored specimen. Lynn Sim photograph.

Realgar, Shimen Arsenic Mine, China. (above left) This is another crystal habit of the bright red sulfur species realgar, which displays stunningly beautiful crystals of a totally different crystallography than the previous specimen can be appreciated better by turning it in your hand and seeing all the crystal flashes. It measures 14 cm wide,10.2 cm tall and 3.8 cm thick. Joe Budd photograph.

Orpiment, Twin Creeks Mine, Nevada, USA. (right) This great discovery along with those found in the Shimen Arsenic mine in China represent the best harvests of this rare species. Specimen measures 7.5 cm tall by 6.4 cm wide. Jeff Scovil photograph.

Carrollite Kamoya South II Mine, West Of Kambove, Katanga, Congo. The Kamoya South II Mine was a literally guarded secret. A mineral invasion was made into the Congo and this locality was held by thousands of armed troops as the valuable cobalt was mined in just a few short years. Collectors would get specimens from the ore piled at the refinery and, because they did not know where the ore was coming from, they labeled the carrollite from locations which may have produced carrollite before, although there were many improbable claims as well. Kamoya South II Mine carrollites may have rare faces and when they do, mislabeled specimens are easy to spot as no other locality has produced some of the forms known there. Some of these carrollites are sitting on a rhombohedral calcite matrix with carrollite crystals more than 2.5 cm high, with only two-thirds of the octahedron protruding from the matrix. Specimen measures 6.4 cm high and 5.6 cm wide.

Skutterudite, Bou Azzer, Morocco. This superb cobalt rich specimen measures 19 cm wide, 10.2 cm high and 6.4 cm thick and flaunts far more than 100 cube and octahedral faces and even includes quartz crystals in the bottom vug. Lynn Sim photograph.

Boulangerite On Quartz – Yaogangxian Mine, China. Boulangerite crystals occur in needles finer than human hair or delicate spider webs, suspended in mid air. Specimen measures 19 cm wide, 12.7 cm deep and 6.4 cm thick. Joe Budd photograph.

Arsenopyrite, Yaogangxian Mine, China. This extremely sculptural arsenopyrite with a 4.4 cm wide quartz crystal backdrop also features serrated edges and a nearly sterling silver patina. Specimen measures 10.2 cm wide, 7.5 cm high and 9.5 cm thick. Joe Budd photograph.

Pyrite, Huanzala, Peru. This one-of-a-kind pyrite specimen from this rich pyrite deposit shows off its beautiful corrugated faces on a series of seven intergrown crystals, some 7.5 cm on an edge. Many pyrites from Huanzala, Peru present flat beveled edges between the cube corners, indicating that the cube was stopped in the process of becoming a cubo-octahedron. A few small surface-lined "cathedral cubed" pyrite cube crystals. Joe Budd photograph.

by Keith Proctor and Mauna Proctor   404

Pyrite, Navajun, Spain. (upper right) This specimen sports seven perfect pyrite cubes on matrix, some intergrown and others as isolated cubes. Specimen measures 7 cm by 7 cm. Joe Budd photograph.

Pyrite, Navajun, Spain. (lower left) Intergrown pyrite cube crystal cluster. measures 7.5 cm x 7 cm x 7.5 cm. From the Dr. Ed David in 1996. Joe Budd photograph.

Pyrite, Huanzala, Peru. (upper right) This 7.5 by 7.5 cm mound is covered completely with small cubes. If we move this specimen in our hands we see nothing but closely packed Pyrite cube-face flashes. Joe Budd photograph.

Pyrite, China. (lower left) 7.5 cm high cluster of brilliant pyrites on a 12.5 by 12.5 by 12.5 cm triangular quartz plate. Lynn Sim photograph.

Pyrite, La Libertad Mine, Quiruvilca, Peru. This highly sculptured cabinet-sized octahedral pyrite cluster (11.4 cm across) was purchased more than 35 years ago, and its luster and superb quality have sustained its superior status throughout the years. The main octahedral crystal is 11.4 cm across, and this specimen was found at Quiruvilca, which also produced some of the biggest and best octahedrons. It is difficult to avoid turning this specimen in your hands to enjoy the perfection of the architectural angles and the striations of the flat octahedral tips that are slightly beveled. Joe Budd photograph.

Pyrite, Huanzala, Peru. This rare growth phenomenon displays bright octahedrons with "mottled faces", indicating that crystal face growth was incomplete. Although two of the flat triangular octahedral faces are incompletely filled in and show only partly finished faces, we still see "filed edges" on the finished parts of the crystal faces. The largest pyrite octahedron (seen center front) illustrates the sequence of crystallization. Specimen measures 8.9 cm wide and 7 cm high. Joe Budd photographs.

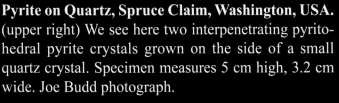

Pyrite on Quartz, Spruce Claim, Washington, USA. (upper right) We see here two interpenetrating pyritohedral pyrite crystals grown on the side of a small quartz crystal. Specimen measures 5 cm high, 3.2 cm wide. Joe Budd photograph.

Pyrite, Huanzala, Peru. (lower right) Pyrite cluster 7.5 cm high,7.5 wide and 5 cm deep/thick; featuring a large cubo-octahedral pyrite sitting on top of smaller pyrite crystals. These cubo-octahedral crystals present fourteen faces on each crystal - six from the original cube form and eight from the bi-pyramidal octahedral form. These faces are uncommon worldwide in nice examples like this. Lynn Sim photograph.

Pyrite, Huanzala, Peru. This "confused" pyrite specimen resembles a surrealistic dog sculpture rendered by Pablo Picaso. "It had a hard life, but it has a lot of interesting stories to tell." On this small specimen measuring 8.9 cm wide, 5 cm tall and 4.4 cm thick/deep there are many crystal faces. We see pyritohedral (five-sided), and cubo-octahedral faces (triangular and six-sided) along with triangular octahedral faces and even one partial 12-sided dodecahedron crystal (one of the legs of this natural dog sculpture). Joe Budd photograph.

Marcasite, Cap Blanc Nez, France. (above left) Viewed here is an atypically excellent marcasite crystal cluster with three or four different shapes of marcasite crystals. Acquired from the Dr. Ed David collection in 1996. There are two growth overlays of marcasites. Marcasite, a polymorph of Pyrite, has an identical formula but with a completely different crystal habit (orthorhombic and not isometric). Specimen is 7 cm wide by 8.9 cm high.
Joe Budd photograph.

Marcasite On Pyrite, Tri-State Region Of USA (below) The spike-like marcasite is deposited on top of pyrite crystals. Specimen measures 10.2 cm wide by 5 cm high. Jeff Scovil photograph.

Pyrrhotite, Nikolai Mine, Dal'negorsk, Russia. Here we see the *pièce de résistance* of pyrrhotites – a well-crystallized display specimen. These clusters of 10.2 cm crystals with several smaller crystals are intermixed with quartz crystals on matrix. The 10.2 cm crystal books are nearly 2.5 cm thick and very shiny. The edges of these two thick crystal books show that they seem to be made up of thin stacked crystals similar to the layered crystals of the micas. The reverse side of this specimen also displays many isolated pyrrhotites. This pyrrhotite, measuring 20.8 wide and 17.6 cm tall, was attached to its wall rock only by a narrow 3.8 cm wide strip of quartz, but the miners managed to pry it off the wall without breaking anything. One of the most critical and tedious processes for the dealers who buy at the source mines is to train the usually careless miners that broken or badly chipped crystals are almost worthless. Saving perfect and beautiful specimens requires that this training process be continually reinforced. Joe Budd photograph.

by Keith Proctor and Mauna Proctor   412

Chalcopyrite, Nikolai Mine, Dal'negorsk, Russia.
(above right) This chalcopyrite crystal group features
a 5 cm high and 4.4 cm wide cluster of sharp crystals
with a small fourteen-sided cubo-octahedron crystal
of galena; this bronze colored crystal sits on a small
sphalerite matrix. Joe Budd photograph.

Chalcopyrite, Huanzala, Peru. (lower left) Golden
bronze colored crystals on shiny pyrite crystals. Specimen measures 10.2 cm by 10.2 cm. Joe Budd photograph.

Chalcopyrite, Dreisler Mine, Germany. (lower
right) Equant chalcopyrite crystals with triangular
faces sprinkled on white barite blades. Entire specimen
measures 22.9 by 17.8 cm. Joe Budd photograph.

Galena Cubes, Madan, Bulgaria. (upper right) Recent to this writing, the mines near Madan city, Bulgaria have produced interesting examples of "skeletal" galena cubes. However, a great controversy has arisen over their origin. The miners say that they have never seen such specimens as these. As the miners are the primary mineral collectors, this is astonishing as, otherwise, there is beginning to be a "supply" of these "skeletal" specimens in the marketplace. Skeptical mineral collectors have even tried to duplicate these odd crystal formations. The most common way is to use an air abrasion unit to carve away the galena. While it may be easy to replicate these crystals artificially, the miners would have even more influence authenticating the naturalness of these specimens. The jury is still out. Specimen measures 10.2 cm wide and 6.4 cm high.
Lynn Sim photograph.

Galena, Sweetwater Mine, Missouri, USA. (lower left) This is an interesting specimen crystalographically. The dominant crystal is the cube, but the associated galenas are octahedral. Note the mirror face on the main galena crystal. Specimen measures 9.5 cm high by 5 cm wide. Joe Budd photograph.

Galena, Sweetwater Mine, Missouri, USA. (lower right) Specimen measures 5 cm by 5 cm. Budd photograph.

Galena, Madan, Bulgaria. Looking closely where the biggest curved cube is visible, we can see at least eight cubes on the top of the specimen displaying twisted and curved cube faces. On the top right side of this specimen are four cubes with truncated "pre-octahedral" (triangular) cube corners; one corner is skeletal leaving a deep triangular "dimple" hole in the center of its corner. The galena crystals otherwise remain relatively sharp. Specimen measures 14 cm wide and 10.2 cm tall (with the biggest wavy cube crystal being on the top). Joe Budd photograph.

Galena, Nikolai Mine, Dal'negorsk, Russia. Seen here is an "atypically" good example of cubo-octahedral galena clusters from Dal'negorsk. This heart-shaped specimen measures 14 cm wide and 11.4 cm high, and the galena crystals are found intermixed with the typical cast of associated minerals, such as sphalerite which provided the "base coat" for the galenas to grow on; then chalcopyrite and thin white needle calcites and the pyrrhotites which formed last. Even the sequence of crystal deposition is often predictable.
Joe Budd photograph.

Galena, Nikolai Mine, Dal'negorsk, Russia. (above left) This galena cubo-octahedral crystal, with quartz crystals at the bottom is very well-formed. Specimen measures 6.4 cm wide, 4.4 cm high and 5 cm deep. Joe Budd photograph.

Galena, Tri-State Region, USA. (right) Because they are so different from most worldwide galenas, fine cubo-octahedral specimens from the famed tri-state region of America (the mining region where the corners of Kansas, Oklahoma and Missouri meet) are very highly sought after and are almost extinct on the market. This specimen is a lovely example. It consists of a 3.8 cm long by 3.2 cm wide beautifully dominant cube crystal with its top cube corners dominated by sculptural cubo-octahedrons that overhang all four corners, thus making this crystal appear bigger. This magnificent assemblage is perched on the corner of a gray colored chert matrix so common to this area. Specimen measures 6.4 cm wide, 7.5 cm deep and 5 cm thick. Joe Budd photograph.

Galena, Tri-State Region, USA. The Proctors have kept and enjoyed this unique single galena crystal (measuring 5 cm wide, 3.8 cm high, and 3.2 cm thick) for over thirty years, because it is a one-of-a-kind masterpiece sculpture. This front view shows stepped octahedrons on the right and an uncommon six-sided flat crystal on top, with fantastic texturing on the front (cube) face. The right side shows the five stepped octahedrons (some with flat points) from a different angle. This single crystal is a "floater" with no apparent point of contact. It reminds us a lot of a Mayan Temple in Central America. Joe Budd photograph.

Galena Spinel Twin With Quartz, Sixteenth of September Mine, Madan, Bulgaria. (above left) This specimen exhibits a brilliant spinel-law-twinned crystal in the center of the crystal cluster, and it is surrounded by quartz crystals on both sides. There is a 7.5 cm wide, oval shaped spinel-twinned crystal structure in the middle of this specimen, and the overall specimen is 11.4 cm wide, 6.4 cm high, and 7.5 cm thick. This crystal goes from 8 o'clock (on the left) to 2 o'clock (on the right), and we are looking at the top of the spinel-twin crystal; the plane/canyon dividing these two halves is really visible. Joe Budd photograph.

Galena, Madan, Bulgaria. (lower right) Seen here is a flat white calcite specimen measuring 14 wide and 10.2 cm deep, and on the top edge of this matrix is a delightful brilliant spinel-twinned galena crystal cluster (measuring 4.4 cm wide) which flashes many shiny and typical triangular faces at us. The dividing line separating the two spinel-twin halves is barely visible, but we can "define" this type crystal because both front and back halves show only triangular galena faces. Joe Budd photograph.

Galena, Madan, Bulgaria. Probably the most beautiful spinel-twin galena crystals from this district were in particularly deep mines. This specimen is 10.2 cm wide with brilliant reflections on the hundreds of flat narrow elongated faces. There are ten very flat wide spinel-twin crystals. Specimen measures 21.6 cm tall, 14 cm wide, and 10.2 cm thick. This amazing lead-rich specimen weighs almost five kilos. Joe Budd photograph.

Stibnite, Guangxi Zhuang Autonomous Region, China. (above) These beautiful stibnite clusters with multiple, isolated blunt tipped compact sprays of crystals sit on top of an 20.3 cm wide white matrix providing a beautiful and stark contrast. Joe Budd photograph.

Stibnite, Xikuangshan Mine, Lengshuijiang, Hunan, China. (right) This delightful stibnite and calcite specimen displays a beautiful composition because a second growth stage of formation encased each stibnite crystal by isolated calcite rhombohedrons. This composition is both delicate and whimsical and it renders a wonderful visual impact because each stibnite crystal is visible through the clear calcite crystals. Crystal group measures 8.3 cm x 7.5 cm.
Joe Budd photograph.

Stibnite, Baia Sprie, Romania. This aesthetic spray of delicate stibnite crystals, measuring 7.5 cm wide, 6.4 cm tall and 5 cm deep/thick explodes from an extremely thin quartz matrix (on the left side). Specimen displays great harmony and rhythm. Joe Budd photograph.

Stibnite, Wushan Antimony Mine, China. There seem to be two consistent major types of stibnite crystal cluster presentations. The previous specimen exhibited the jack-straw criss-crossing type, and this specimen displays the dramatic, soaring type. Specimen measures 27.9 cm by 14 cm wide. James Elliot photograph.

Stibnite, Wushan Antimony Mine, China. China has certainly produced stibnite crystals that eclipse any earlier examples. Because of their brilliant sheen, soaring crystals with stunning terminations, and their dramatic presentation the best stibnite clusters are awe-inspiring. Specimen measures 15.2 cm wide and 20.3 tall. Jeff Scovil photograph.

by Keith Proctor and Mauna Proctor 424